Introduction to Biological Latin and Greek
Combined with
Origins from Mythology of Biological Names and Terms

Dr. Patrick H. Yancey, S.J.

Professor and Chairman of
Department of Biology
Spring Hill College

First Edition of the Combined Reprints
1999

Published by

William Enderle Roberts, M.D.

Reprinted under license from the
Spring Hill College Press, Mobile, AL.

Reprinted by Mississippi Printing Company, Greenwood, Mississippi

First Printing Bios XV #1 1944
1st Edition -- 1944   LCCN 45-18801
2nd Edition -- 1945   LCCN 47-1539
3rd Edition -- 1946
4th Edition -- 1950   LCCN 54-30131
Revised and Enlarged
5th Edition -- 1959

Library of Congress Catalog Card Number 99-74238

ISBN 0-9672426-0-6

Introduction to Biological Latin and Greek

INTRODUCTION

The first scientific study of nature was undertaken by the Greek philosophers, especially Aristotle, who has justly been called the "Father of Biology." His treatises, "On the Nature of Animals" and others, are the earliest examples of a specifically biological literature, and his classification of animals remained in vogue until the time of Linnaeus. Hence the science of biology started off with a distinctly Grecian terminology.

This work was continued, more particularly in the field of medicine, by the Roman physicians, such as Galen, who gave to many of the original Greek terms a Latin form and added many more purely Latin words to the vocabulary of biology. During the Middle Ages, the works of Aristotle were translated into Latin and much of his terminology was retained in a Latin dress. At that time also and on down into modern times, Latin was the language of the schools and all scientific works were written in that language. After Latin was abandoned as the medium of instruction, biologists were still educated along classical lines and, consequently, described their discoveries in terms borrowed from the classical languages. Moreover, Latin provided a universally understandable medium for expressing ideas, especially for the naming of plants and animals which do not conform to man-made national boundaries. This last use of Graeco-Latin terminology was securely fixed by the "Systema Naturae" of Carl von Linné better known under his Latin name, Linnaeus.

Thus it has come about that most of the terms used in biology and medicine today are derived from Latin or Greek, those from the latter usually having been changed into a Latin form. This Graeco-Latin vocabulary, which proved so helpful in an earlier day, has, with the decline of classical education, proved rather a stumbling block to students of biology. For, today, very few study Latin (or, at least, enough to be of any help) and practically none, Greek; therefore the terminology of science is mostly a meaningless jargon. Every term has to be learned parrot-fashion and is soon forgotten.

In an effort to remedy this situation the author has prepared this briefest adequate summary of the main facts and forms of the Latin and Greek languages which will be useful for students of the biological sciences in the hope that it will give them a linguistic foundation for better work in these sciences. The work is divided into four sections: Latin; Greek; Biological Nomenclature; and Some Common Latin and Greek Roots and Terms. Regarding the first two, while the two languages must necessarily be discussed separately; however, since most Greek words have come to us through the Latin, no attempt will be made to distinguish them as to origin in these parts and examples from both languages will be used indiscriminately.

LATIN

1. THE ALPHABET. The Latin alphabet is the same as the English, except that it does not contain the letters *j*, *v*, and *w*. *K* occurs in a few words, having been largely substituted for by *C*. *Z* is found only in words from the Greek. *I* and *U* were used both as vowels and consonants. When used as consonants they are written and printed *J* and *V* in modern scientific words, e.g. *major, vermis*.

2. PRONUNCIATION. Scholars are not agreed on all the details of the Roman pronunciation of Latin, hence almost every nationality has its own way of pronouncing this language. It is beyond the scope of this work to discuss pronunciation in detail. Suffice it to say that in scientific circles among the English-speaking peoples an "English" pronunciation of Latin and latinized Greek has become widespread. For details of this "English Method" consult Muldoon, *Lessons in Pharmaceutical Latin and Prescription Writing and Interpretation* (New York, 1937). The following are the main points.

1) The vowels *a*, *e*, *i*, *y*, *o*, and *u* are usually pronounced long when stressed or final, e.g., *cāva, sērum, mēdiastinum, cÿanĭdum, rōsa, ūterus* and *bacilli*. But when they stand before two consonants they are pronounced short, e.g., *extrăctum, ascĕndens, intĕrnus, ŏssis, colŭmna*, unless one of the two consonants is *l*, *r* or *h*, in which case they may be long, e.g., *cītricum*. They may also be short when they end an accented syllable, e.g., *gelă'tinum*.

2) The dipthongs *ae* and *oe*, and also the ie of words of the fifth declension, are pronounced like *ee*, e.g., *tunicae* (tunisee), *coecum* (seecum), *species* (speeshees). The diphthong *au* is sounded like awe, e.g., *cauda* (cawda). The diphthong *eu* of Greek words is pronounced as long *u*, e.g., *Euchordata* (ūcordata).

3) Consonants are pronounced as in English. For instance, *c* and *g* are hard before *a*, *o*, *u*, the diphthong *au* and all consonants, e.g., *cava, corona, cutis, cauda, cloaca* and *galea, Gordius, gubernaculum, gaudium, glans*. They are pronounced soft before *i*, *e*, *y*, and the diphthongs *ae, oe*, and *eu*, e.g., *cervix, circum, cyanidum, caecum*, or *coecum, pharmaceuticum* and *genu, gingiva, gyrus*.

Final *s* is often pronounced like *z*, e.g., *pars* (parz); and *es* like *ease*, eg., *fomes* (foamease).

Ch is pronounced *K*, e.g. *chara* (kara), *branchia* (brankia).

4) A Latin word has as many syllables as it contains vowels or diphthongs and generally every syllable is pronounced, e.g., *mediale* (mee-dee-ā'lee). However, there are many exceptions, as *species* above.

5) Most latin words used in biology have the accent on the penult or next to the last syllable, e.g., *ascen'dens, exter'nus*. But, *mi'nimus* and *-is'simus*.

3. WORD FORMATION. Latin words are composed of two parts: 1) an invariable *root* or *stem*; and 2) a variable *ending*. The variations in the latter indicate the different functional uses and meanings of the word as to gender, number, and case. Thus the word *rosa* (rose) has the stem *ros-* and the endings: singular, *a, ae, ae, am, a, a*; and plural, *ae, arum, is, as, ae, is*. However, for the biologist, only one or, at most, two endings are important.

4. DECLENSIONS. Latin nouns are divided into five *declensions* according to the kind of endings they have. Each declension has six *cases* in both singular and plural: Nominative, Genitive, Dative, Accusative, Vocative, and Ablative. However, only two of these are needed by the biologist: the Nominative which is equivalent to the subjective case in English and merely names the thing; and the Genitive which signifies possession and corresponds to the possessive case in English and is translated by the preposition "of" or the apostrophe *'s*.

Attention must be called to the fact that the stem is not always contained in the Nominative. Sometimes, too, the Nominative varies in the same declension. This is signified in the table below by "var." The endings of the Nominative and Genitive singular and plural of the five declensions with examples and some uses of the Genitive of words occurring in biology are given in the following table. Some declensions have more than one form; these are indicated by subdivisions. The stem and ending are separated by a hyphen and separated endings are preceded by a hyphen. The English plural is placed in parenthesis after the singular.

5. DIMINUTIVES. Many biological names are diminutives signifying smaller size than that of the primitive. In Latin diminutives end in *-olus, -ulus, -ellus,* and *-culus*. They are of the same gender as their primitives. They are anglicized into *-ole, -ule, -elle, -cule,* and *-cle*. They usually follow these rules:

1) Diminutives in *-olus, -ulus,* and *-ellus* are formed from primitives of the first and second declensions in the following manner:

a) When the stem of the primitive ends in a vowel, the ending *-olus* is added to it, e.g., *nucle-olus, besti-ola*. English forms: *arteriole, centriole*.

b) When the stem of the primitive ends in a consonant, the ending *-ulus* is added to it, e.g., *hort-ulus, lun-ula, capit-ulum*. English forms: *venule, plumule*.

c) When the stem of the primitive ends in *l, n,* or *r* it is generally contracted, and then the ending *-ellus* is added to it, e.g., *oc-ellus* (from *ocul-us*), *as-ellus* (from *asin-us*). English form: *organelle*.

2) Diminutives in *-culus* are formed from primitives of the third and fourth declensions, as follows:

a) When the stem ends in *r*, the ending *-culus* is added to the nominative, e.g., *flos-culus, mulier-cula*.

b) When the stem does not end in *r*, the ending *-culus* is added to it by means of the connective vowel *i*, e.g., *fasc-i-culus, fun-i-culus, nav-i-cula, ret-i-culum*. English forms: *fasicle, reticule*.

Declension	Endings		Examples and Uses of Genitive
	Singular	Plural	
I. Nom.	-a	-ae	ros-a, -ae; rose(s)
Gen.	-ae	-arum	ros-ae, -arum; of the rose(s)
			levator scapulae -- levator of the shoulder
			levatores costarum -- levators of the ribs
II. 1. Nom.	-us	-i	bacill-us, -i, little rod(s)
Gen.	-i	-orum	bacill-i, -orum; of the little rod(s)
			abductor digiti -- abductor of the finger
			flexor digitorum -- flexor of the fingers
2. Nom.	-um	-a	cili-um, -a; eyelid(s)
Gen.	-i	-orum	cili-i, -orum; of the eyelid(s)
			ampulla recti -- ampulla of the rectum
			commissura labiorum -- commissure of the lips
III. 1. Nom.	var.	-es	homo, homin-es; man (men)
			dens, dent-es; tooth (teeth)
Gen.	-is	-um	homin-is, -um; of the man (men)
			or the man's (men's)
	-is	-ium	dent-is, -ium; of the tooth (teeth)
			cavum dentis -- socket of the tooth
			juncturae tendinum -- junctions of tendons
2. Nom.	var.	-a	caput, capit-a; head(s)
		-ia	animal, animal-ia; living thing(s)
Gen.	-is	-um	capit-is, -um; of the head(s)
	-is	-ium	animal-is, -ium; of the living thing(s)
			semispinalis capitis -- semispinal muscle of the head
			Historia Animalium -- The History of Living Things
IV. 1. Nom.	-us	-us	sin-us, -us; bay(s)
Gen.	-us	-uum	sin-us, -uum; of the bay(s)
			valvula sinus coronarii -- valve of the coronary sinus
			confluens sinuum -- confluence of sinuses
2. Nom.	-u	-ua	genu-a, -ua; knee(s)
Gen.	-us	-uum	gen-us, -uum; of the knee(s)
			articulatio genus -- the knee joint
			bulbi cornuum -- bulbs of the horns
V. Nom.	-es	-es	faci-es, -es; face(s)
Gen.	-ei	-erum	faci-ei, -erum; of the face(s)
			nervus faciei -- nerve of the face
			origo specierum -- origin of species

c)   Primitives in *es* generally drop *s* and add *-cula*, e.g., *vulpe-cula* (from *vulp-es*), *mole-cula* (from *mol-es*). English form: *molecule*.

d)   Primitives in *o* change the stem syllables *on* and *in* into *un*, e.g., *homun-culus* (from *homo*, *homin-is*), *virgun-cula* (from *virgo*, *virgin-is*).

3)   No fixed rule: *cat-ellus* (from *catul-us*), *Dorid-ella* and *Doridun-culus* (from *Doris*), *furun-culus* (from *fur*), *Ranun-culus* (from *Rana*), *vas-culum* (from *vas*), *cor-olla* and *coron-ella* (from *corona*).

6.   AGREEMENT OF ADJECTIVES.   Many biological terms, especially the specific names of organisms and the names of bones, muscles, etc., are often adjectives expressing some characteristic of the organism or part. There are three groups of adjectives in Latin, namely, those having:

1)   *Three endings* distinct for masculine, feminine, and neuter genders which may be either: *-us*, *-a*, *-um*, e.g., *bon-us*, *bon-um*; or *-er*, *-is*, *-e*, e.g., *ac-er*, *acr-is*, *acr-e*.

2)   *Two endings*, one for the masculine and feminine and the other for the neuter, namely, *-is* and *-e*, e.g., *grav-is*, *grav-e*.

3)   *One ending* for all genders, usually *ns* or *x*, e.g., *sapiens*, *simplex*.

Adjectives must agree in gender, number, and case with the nouns they modify, consequently the specific name of an organism must have the same gender as the generic name (they are usually singular nominatives). Thus the common house cat belongs to the genus *Felis* which is a feminine noun. Therefore the adjective used as the specific name must be feminine, namely, *domestica* (from *domus* -- house).   On the other hand the dog belongs to the genus *Canis* which is masculine, hence the specific names of the various species of dogs must be masculine adjectives, e.g., *C. rufus* -- the red wolf; *C. familiaris* -- the domesticated dog; *C. latrans* -- the coyote. The genus *Paramecium* is neuter, therefore all species of paramecium should be neuter adjectives, e.g., *P. caudatum*, *P. multimicronucleatum* (not multi-micronucleata as some authors call it).

The Latin word for bone is os (ossa), a neuter noun.   Therefore, adjectives used as the names of specific bones should be in the neuter, e.g., *os innominatum* (*ossa innominata*).   However, many bones are named from the part of the body where they are found. In that case the specific name is in the genitive case of the part where they are located, e.g., *os cordis* -- the bone of the heart (*cor*, *cord-is*). *Ligamentum* (*ligamenta*) -- ligament(s) is similar, e.g., *ligamentum latum*, *ligamenta flava*, *ligamentum nuchae*.

The word for muscle is *musculus* (*musculi*), a masculine word of the second declension.   Adjectives used as the names of muscles must be masculine and in the singular or plural, according as one or more than one muscle is referred to, e.g., *musculus interosseus* (*musculi interossei*) -- the muscle(s) between the bones of the fingers. In most cases the word *musculus* is omitted or abbreviated to *m.*, and the adjective alone used as the name of the muscle, e.g., *flexor communis* (*flexores communes*). *Nervus* (*nervi*) -- nerve(s) follows the same rule, e.g., *nervus splanchnicus*, *nervus radialis*.

The words for artery and vein, *arteria* and *vena*, are feminine words of the first declension. Adjectives used as the names of arteries and veins must be feminine singular or plural as the case may be, e.g., *arteria iliaca, externa, vena cava, arteriolae rectae, venae stellatae.* Again the words *arteria* and *vena* are often omitted and the adjectives alone used, e.g., *carotis interna.*

7. COMPARISON OF ADJECTIVES. In some cases the comparative or superlative degree of adjectives is used to signify greater or lesser size or importance. The comparative degree is formed by adding the endings *-ior (iores)* for the masculine and feminine, and *-ius (iora)* for the neuter to the stem of the positive, e.g., *m. carpi radialis brevior* (from brev-is), *ligamentum cruciatum posterius* (from posterus, -a, -um).

However, in many cases the irregular comparatives *major (-es)*, masculine and feminine, and *majus (majora)*, neuter (from magnus, -a, -um) and *minor (-es)* or *minus (minora)*, are added to the noun, e.g., *m. pectoralis major* and *minor, os multangulum majus* and *minus.*

The superlative degree is formed by adding *-issimus, -a, -um* or *-imus, -a, -um* to the positive, e.g., *m. latissimus* (from latus) *dorsi.* Sometimes the irregular superlative forms *maximus, -a, -um* (from magnus) and *minimus, -a, -um* (from parvus), are added to the noun, e.g., *m. glutaeus maximus, nervus splanchnicus minimus, venae cordis minimae.*

8. NUMERALS may be *cardinals* (one, two, three), *ordinals* (first, second, third), *distributives* (one by one, two by two, three by three), or *adverbials* (once, twice, thrice). With the exception of the first three cardinals and all of the ordinals and distributives, numerals are indeclinable adjectives. The first twelve, hundred, and thousand are of most frequent occurrence.

	Cardinals	Ordinals	Distributives	Adverbials
I	unus, -a, -um	primus, -a, -um	singuli, -ae, -a	semel
II	duo, duae, duo	secundus	bini	bis
III	tres, tria	tertius	terni	ter
IV	quattuor	quartus	quarterni	quater
V	quinque	quintus	quini	quinquies
VI	sex	sextus	seni	sexies
VII	septem	septimus	septeni	septies
VIII	octo	octavus	octoni	octies
IX	novem	nonus	noveni	novies
X	decem	decimus	deni	decies
XI	undecim	undecimus	undeni	undecies
XII	duodecim	duodecimus	duodeni	duodecies
C	centum	centesimus	centeni	centies
M	mille, -ia	millesimus	singula millia	millies

GREEK

1. THE ALPHABET. The letters of the Greek alphabet have about the same sounds as those of Latin but are named and written somewhat differently. Scientific words from Greek are usually in Latin form but since

THE GREEK ALPHABET

Form		Sound	Name	
A	α	*a* in far	ἄλφα	alpha
B	β	*b*	βῆτα	beta
Γ	γ	*g* in go	γάμμα	gamma
Δ	δ	*d*	δέλτα	delta
E	ε	*ĕ* in met	εἰ, ἒ ψῑλόν	epsilon
Z	ζ	*dz*	ζῆτα	zeta
H	η	*ey* in obey	ἦτα	eta
Θ	θ	*th* in thin	θῆτα	theta
I	ι	*i* in machine	ἰῶτα	iota
K	κ	*k*	κάππα	kappa
Λ	λ	*l*	λάμβδα	lambda
M	μ	*m*	μθ	mu
N	ν	*n*	νθ	nu
Ξ	ξ	*ks, x* in flax	ξεῖ, ξῖ	xi
O	o	*ŏ* in renovate	οὖ, ὂ μῑκρόν	omicron
Π	π	*p*	πεῖ, πῖ	pi
P	ρ	*r*	ῥῶ	rho
Σ	σ ς	*s* in see	σίγμα	sigma
T	τ	*t* in to	ταῦ	tau
Y	υ	French *u*, German *ü*	ῦ, ῦ ψῑλόν	upsilon
Φ	φ	*ph* in physics	φεῖ, φῖ	phi
X	χ	German *ch*	χεῖ, χῖ	chi
Ψ	ψ	*ps*	ψεῖ, ψῖ	psi
Ω	ω	*ō* in no	ὦ, ὦ μέγα	omega

The initial sound of the name (last column) gives the sound of the letter.

Greek letters are often used to designate formulae and divisions they are herewith transcribed with their names, sounds, and English equivalents.

2. PRONUNCIATION. The same may be said of Greek as was said of Latin pronunciation. The "English Method" is usually followed in scientific circles.

3. WORD FORMATION. Similar to Latin.

4. DECLENSIONS. There are three declensions in Greek which correspond roughly with the I, II, and III declensions of Latin, some of whose endings are substituted for those of the Greek in scientific terminology

Declension   Endings   **Examples and Uses of Genitive**

	Singular			Plural	

I. Nom. -a   -ai   (ae)   cardi-a; -ai; heart(s) -- *cardiac*
          -e   (a)   -ai   (ae)   cephal-e, -ai; head(s) -- *cardiac*
   Gen. -as   (ae) -on   (arum) cardi-as, -on; of the heart(s)
          -es   (ae) -on   (arum) cephal-es; -on; of the head(s)

II. 1. Nom. -os   (us) -oi   (i)   bi-os, -oi; life (lives) -- *biology*
    Gen.   -ou   (i)   -on   (orum)   bi-ou, -on; of the life (lives)
   2. Nom.   -on   (um) -a   gangli-on, -a; swelling(s)
    Gen.   -ou   (i)   -on   (orum)   gangli-ou (i), -on (orum); of the
                                        swelling(s)
                                        Radices ganglii ciliaris

III. 1. Nom. -ps   -es   phleps, phleb-es; vein(s) -- *phlebitis*
              -x   -es   pharynx, pharyng-es; throat(s)
              -is   -es   epididymis, epididymid-es
                                  physis, -es (eis); growth(s)
              -as   -es   gigas, gigant-es; giant(s) -- *gigantism*
              -on   -es   geron, geront-es; old man (men)
      Gen.   -os (is) -on (um) phleb-os, -on; of the vein(s)
              -os (is) -on (um) pharyng-os (is), -on (um); of the
                                    throat(s)
                                    -- *Raphe pharyngis*
              -os (is) -on (um) epididymid-os (is), -on (um) --
                                    Ligamentum epididymidis;
                                    Decussatio pyramidum
              -os (is) -on (um) phys-eos (is), -on (ium) -- *Fossa*
                                    hypophyseos, Facies symphyseos
      2. Nom. -a   -a   chiasma, chiasmat-a; crossing(s)
               -ar   -a   hepar, hepat-a; liver(s) -- *hepatic*
               -as   -a   keras, kerat-a; horn(s) -- *keratin*
       Gen.   -os (is) -on (um) chiasmat-os (is); -on (um) -- *Cisterna*
                                     chiasmatis
               -os (is) -on (um) hepat-os (is), -on (um) -- *Porta hepatis*
      3. Nom. -er   -es   ther, ther-es; beast(s) -- *therapsida*
                                   gaster, gastr-es; belly(ies) -- *gastric*
                                   aner, andr-es; man (men) -- *androgen*
               -is   -es   rhis, rhin-es; nose(s) -- *rhinoceros*
                                   ornis, ornith-es; bird(s) -- *ornithology*
               -on   -es   axon, axon-es; axle(s) -- *axonal*
       Gen.   -os (is) -on (um) ther-os, -on; of the beast(s)
               -os (is) -on (um) gastr-os, -on; of the belly(ies)
               -os (is) -on (um) andr-os, -on; of the man (men)
               -os (is) -on (um) rhin-os, -on; of the nose(s)
               -os (is) -on (um) axon-os, -on; of the axle(s)
      4. Nom. -ys   -es   ichthys, ichthy-es; fish(es)
       Gen.   -os   -on   ichthy-os, -on; of the fish(es) --
                                   Ichthyology

(indicated below in parentheses). Each declension has several forms but only the more common ones occurring in scientific words are transliterated here with examples and some uses of the genitives. The nominative singular, especially in the III declension, often does not show the stem. There are a number of words which do not fit into any of the above forms. A few of biological significance are given here.

odous, odont-es; tooth (teeth) -- odontology
pous, pod-es; foot (feet) -- podagra, podiatry, pseudopod
ous, ot-a; ear(s) -- otis, otology
cheir, cheir-es; hand(s) -- chiropodist, Chiroptera
phos, phot-es; light(s) -- phosphorescence, phototropism
thrix, trich-es; hair(s) -- Ulothrix, trichocyst
coccyx, coccyg-es; cuckoo(s) -- coccyx, coccygeal

5. NUMERALS in Greek are divided into *cardinals, ordinals,* and *adverbials.* The first four cardinals and the ordinals are declinable. Most of the cardinals are expressed by the letters of the alphabet.

	Cardinals	**Ordinals**	**Adverbials**
1	heis, mia, hen	protos, e, on	hapax
2	duo	deuteros, a, on	dis
3	treis, tria	tritos, e, on	tris
4	tettares, -a	tetartos	tetrakis
5	pente	pemptos	pentakis
6	hex	hektos	hexakis
7	hepta	hebdomos	heptakis
8	okto	ogdoös	oktakis
9	ennea	enatos	enakis
10	deka	dekatos	dekakis
11	hendeka	hendekatos	hendekakis
12	dodeka	dodekatos	dodekakis
100	hekaton	hekatostos	hekatontakis
1000	chilioi, -ai, -a	chiliostos	chiliakis
10000	murioi, -ai, -a (also taken as any *large number,* hence *myriad*)		

BIOLOGICAL NOMENCLATURE

Linnaeus was the founder of our modern system of classification of plants and animals. He classified them according to four categories: *Class, Order, Genus,* and *Species.* Since his time two other principal categories have been added, the *Phylum* and the *Family,* and several sub-categories. Linnaeus also introduced the *binomial system* of nomenclature, according to which every plant and animal is given two names, the *generic,* beginning with a capital letter, and the *specific,* usually beginning with a small letter.

PLANTS

1. PHYLA OR SUBKINGDOMS. There are only four. Their names are compound words, the first part expressing the characteristic of the phylum and the second, the plural of the Greek noun for plants, *phyla.* Thus

Thallophyta, Bryophyta, Pteridophyta, Spermatophyta.   Phyta is often
anglicized to "phytes" and the plants referred to as *Thallophytes*, etc.
   2.   CLASSES AND SUBCLASSES.   Their names usually have the plural
ending of the Latin first declension, *ae*, e.g., *Angiospermae* and *Dicotyle-
doneae.*   But there are exceptions, e.g., *Schizomycetes, Musci.*
   3.   ORDERS.   Adjectives ending in *ales* usually from the name of the
principal genus, e.g., *Rosales* from *Rosa.*
   4.   FAMILIES.   Adjectives ending in *ae* (usually -- *aceae*) from either
the name of the principal genus, e.g., *Rosaceae* from *Rosa*, or some characteristic of most of the genera, e.g., *Leguminosae*, possessing legumes or
pods.
   5.   GENERA.   1) Nouns, often the original Greek or Latin names,
e.g., *Pinus, Rosa, Triticum.*
         2) Descriptive adjectives, e.g., *Trifolium.*
         3) Personal names in adjective form, ending in *ia*, e.g., *Rickettsia*,
from Ricketts who discovered these organisms.
   5.   SPECIES.   1) Adjectives signifying some characteristic feature
like color (*albus, -a, -um; niger, -ra, -rum*), size (*giganteus, -a, -um; nanus,
-a, -um*), incidence (*communis, -e, vulgaris, -e*), edibility (*sativus, -a, -um*),
miscellaneous (*mirabilis, tenax*).   The specific name usually agrees in
gender and number with the generic.   Most species of trees have names
ending in *a* regardless of the ending of the genus because tree in Latin is
feminine, e.g., *Quercus alba, Pinus resinosa.*   But, *Pinus strobus.*
         2) Nouns in apposition, e.g., *Oenothera gigas, Nicotiana tabacum.*
         3) Genitive endings of latinized personal or other names, e.g.,
Prunus besseyi from the botanist Bessey; *Puccinia graminis*, a parasite of
grasses (gramen, graminis).

ANIMALS

   1.   PHYLA AND SUBPHYLA.   Usually neuter plurals of Greek or Latin
nouns and adjectives ending in *a* or *ata* (cf. Word List), e.g., *Protozoa,
Chordata, Vertebrata.*   Exceptions are some phyla of worms whose names
end in *helminthes* (G. worms), e.g., *Platyhelminthes.*
   2.   CLASSES AND SUBCLASSES.   Usually neuter plurals of nouns or
adjectives ending in *a, ea* or *ina*, e.g., *Mastigophora, Arachnoidea, Vol-
vocina.*   But, *Elasmobranchii, Pisces, Aves.*
   3.   ORDERS AND SUBORDERS.   1) Neuter plural adjectives ending in *a*
or *ina*, e.g., *Diptera, Amoebina.*   2) Masculine plural nouns of the second
declension ending in *i*, e.g., *Chrondrostei.*   3) Feminine plural nouns of the
first declension, ending in *ae*, e.g., *Hydromedusae.*   4) Birds and some
fishes: the name of the principal genus ending with *i* plus "formes," e.g.,
Passeriformes, Cypriniformes.
   4.   FAMILIES.   Usually feminine adjective plural forms of generic
names ending in *idae*, e.g., *Canidae, Felidae.*
   5.   GENERA AND SPECIES.   Named like those of plants.

SOME COMMON LATIN AND GREEK ROOTS
AND TERMS

Many biological terms are compound words made up of two or more Latin or Greek words or roots. In this composition, frequently changes in letters are made for the sake of euphony. Thus, sometimes, there is elision of a vowel when the first component ends in a vowel and the second begins with a vowel or diphthong, e.g., *Parophthalmia* from *para* and *ophthalmia*. A final consonant of the first component often undergoes changes. For example, the *n* of *con* (cum) becomes *l* with followed by *l*, e.g., *collusion*; it becomes *m* before *b, m, f, ph*, and *ps*, e.g., *commissure*; and it becomes *r* before *r*, e.g., *correlative*.

In the following list, unless the original Greek or Latin word is commonly used as such, only the combining form is given, followed by a dash when it is the first component of a compound word or a prefix, and preceded by a dash when it is the second component or suffix. In some cases it is used in both ways. Separated endings are also preceded by a cash. (G) or (L) signifies Greek or Latin origin.

a-, an- (G) -- not, without -- abiogenesis, anamniote
a-, ab-, abs- (L) -- away from -- aversion, abductor, abstract
acinus, -i (L) -- berry, grape -- acinous, aciniform
acro- (G) -- at the end or top -- acrocarpous, acrodont, acromion
actin- (G) -- ray -- actinic, Actinomyces
acanth- (G) -- thorn -- acantha, Acanthias, acantho-
ad (L) -- to, towards -- adductor. When used as a prefix the d is sometimes changed to the first consonant of the following word, e.g., acclimate, afferent, assimilate. As a suffix it means towards the part of the body indicated by the word to which it is suffixed, e.g., cephalad, towards the head; caudad, towards the tail.
aden (G) -- gland -- adenase, adenin, adeno-, adenoid
adip- (L) -- fat -- adipose, adiposo-
aer (G) -- air -- aerobe, anaerobic, anaerobiosis
-agogue (G) -- carrying away, drive out -- cholagogue, chloragogue
ala (L) -- wing -- alar, alate, aliform, alisphenoid
albus, -a, -um (L) -- white -- linea alba, corpus albicans, tunica albuginea
alg- (G) -- pain -- algesia, neuralgia, analgesic
all- (G) -- other -- allergy, allometric
allant- (G) -- sausage -- allantois, allanto-, allantoin
allelon- (G) -- of one another -- allele, allelomorphic, parallel
alveolus, -i (L) -- little tub or belly -- alveolar, alveolo-
amb- (L) -- both, on both sides -- ambivalent, amboceptor
amph- (G) -- same as **amb** -- amphiaster, amphibian, amphoteric
ampulla, -ae (L) -- little flash -- a. chyli, aa. of Lorenzini, ampule
amyl- (G) -- starch -- amylase, amylopsin, paramylum
ana (G) -- up, back, anew, again -- anabolism, anaphase
andr- (G) -- man -- androgen, gynander
angl- (G) -- vessel -- angioblast, angiocarpous, angiosperm
ankyl- (G) -- curved -- ankylosis, Ankylostoma
annulus, -i (L) -- ring -- a. abdominalis, annular, Annelida

-ans (L. present participial ending of first conjugation) -ing -- Canis latrans (barking), Latrodectus mactans (killing)
ansa, -ae (L) -- handle -- a. vitellina, a. capitis, ansate, ansiform
ante (L) -- before, in front of antebrachium
anterior, -ius (L) -- fore, going before -- vena cava anterior, antero-
anth- (G) -- flower -- anther, Anthozoa, Helianthus
anthrop- (G) -- man -- anthropology, anthropoid, Pithecanthropus
anti (G) -- opposite, against -- antiseptic, antigen, antibody
anticus (L) -- same as anterior -- tibalis anticus
antrum, -a (L) -- cavity -- a. auris, antral, antro-
apex, apic- (L) -- tip, point -- apical
apo- (G) -- from, off from -- aponeurosis, apochromatic
aqu- (L) -- water -- aquarium, aquatic, aqueous humor
arachn- (G) -- spider -- Arachnida, arachnoid, Arachnoidea
arbor (L) -- tree -- Arbor Vitae, arboreal, arboretum
arc- (L) -- bow, bent -- arciform, Arcoptera, arcuate
arch- (G) -- beginning, primitive, ancient -- archenteron, Archeopteryx
area (L) -- open space -- a. opaca, areolar, areola, areatus
argent- (L) -- silver -- argentaffin, argentine, argentation
argyr- (G) -- silver -- argyrol, argyrophil, argyria
-aria (L) -- suffix denoting "like" or "connected with" -- Utricularia
-arium (L) -- suffix denoting place of a thing -- aquarium, herbarium
arrheno -- (G) -- male -- arrhenoblastoma, arrhenotocia
arthron (G) -- joint -- Arthropod, arthritis, arthrodial, arthrosis
articul- (L) -- connect -- articular, articulate, articulatio, articulus
artio- (G) -- even number -- artiodactyla
aryten (G) -- ladle -- arytenoid cartilage
asc- (G) -- bottle, bag, bladder -- Ascidian, ascon, Ascomycetes, ascus
ascendens (L) going up -- aorta ascendens
-ase (uncertain, possibly G. **-asis**) -- suffix to word denoting substrate and signifying an enzyme acting on that substrate, e.g., zymase, sucrase
aster, astr- (G) -- star -- amphiaster, Asterias, astrocyte
-ata (L) -- neuter plural ending of perfect participle used as suffix to name of some structure and signifying a group of organisms characterized by that structure, e.g., Chordata, Vertebrata
-ate -- English form of above, e.g., Chordate, Vertebrate. Also used as an adjective -- septate, punctate
atel- (G. a -- not tele -- end) -- imperfect, incomplete -- atelia, atelosis, atelocardia
atres-, atret- (G. a -- not tresis -- hole) -- atresia, atretic
atrium, -a (L) -- entrance, room -- atrial, atriopore
audi- (L) -- hear -- audition, auditory
aur- (L) -- 1) air -- auroduct, Aurophysa; 2) ear -- auripuncture; 3) gold -- aureus, Aurococcus
auricul- (L) -- dim. of auris -- ear -- auricle, auricular
auto- (G) -- self -- autonomic, auto-intoxication
ax- (L) -- combining form signifying aggressive, e.g., audax, pugnax
aux- (G) -- growth, increase -- auxin, auxospore
avis, -es (L) -- bird -- avian, aviary
axis (L) -- axle-tree -- axial, epaxial, hypaxial
axon (G) -- same -- axocyte, axonal
bacill- and **bacul-** (L) -- staff, rod -- bacillus (i), Bacularia

bacter-, bactr- (G) -- same -- bacterium (a), Bactridium
baro (G) -- weight -- barometer, barotropism
basidi- (G) -- pedestal -- basidium, Basidiomycetes, basidiospore
basil- (G) -- king, royal, important -- basilic, Basiliscus
basis, -es (G) -- base, bottom -- basilar, basipodite
bath-, bathy- (G) -- depth or height -- Bathornis, bathyspere
bio- (G) -- life -- bioblast, biology, Dermatobia
bis, bi-, bin- (L) -- double, twice -- bisiliac, bilateral, binocular
blast- (G) -- bud, sprout, germ -- blastoderm, osteoblast
blephar- (G) -- eyelid -- blepharal, Blepharisma, blepharoplast
brachium, -a (L) -- arm -- brachial, brachio-
brachy- (G) -- short -- brachydactyly, brachycephalic
brady- (G) -- slow -- bradycardia
branch- (G) -- gill -- branchia, branchial, Lamellibranch, branchio-
bronchus, -i (G) -- air tubes -- bronchial, bronchoscope
brevis, -e (L) -- short, caput breve, breviflex, breviradiate
bryo- (G) -- moss -- bryology, Bryophyta, Bryozoa
bucca, -ae (L) -- cheek -- buccal, buccinator, bucco-
bulla, -ae (L) -- bubble -- bulla tympanica, bullate
bursa, -ae (L) -- pouch -- b. omentalis, bursate, bursitis
butyr- (G) -- butter -- butyrate, butyrin, butyro-
cac- (G) -- bad -- cachexia, cacophony
cad- (L) -- fall -- cadaver, caducous
caecum (L) -- also **cecum** -- blind -- foramen caecum
caen- (G) -- recent -- caenozoic. See **cene**. Also spelled **kaen, ken**
calor (L) -- heat -- calory, calorific, calorimeter
calx, calc- (L) -- chalk, the heel -- calcaneo-, calcaneus, calcar, calcium
calyx, calyc- (G) -- cup -- calycine, calyculus
capill- (L) -- hair -- capillary
caput, capit- (L) -- head -- caput longum m. bicipitis, capitulum, capitellum;
    in combination shortened to **ceps, cip-** -- biceps (bicipites), triceps,
    quadriceps
carpus, -i (L) -- wrist -- carpal, carpectomy, carpo-
caryo- (G) -- nut, nucleus -- caryophage, Caryophyllaceae, caryopsis, acaryocyte
cata (G) -- down -- catabolism, catalyst. Also spelled **kata**
cecum same as **caecum** above -- c. vestibulare, cecal, ceco-
cel- or **coel-** (G) -- hollow, belly -- celiac, celio- celitis
cele (G) -- tumor, hernia -- celosomia, hydrocele
celi- (G) -- belly -- celiac, celiotomy. Also **coel**
cella, -ae (L) -- small chamber -- c. media, cell, cellula, cellulo-
cen- (G) -- empty, void -- cenosis. Also **ken** -- kenophobia
cene (G) -- same as **caen** -- cenogenesis, pliocene. Also **kene**
centrum (G) -- center -- centrifuge, centroacinar, centriole
cephale (G) -- head -- cephalic, encephalon
cept- (L) -- received -- receptor, exteroceptive
cera (L) -- wax -- cerumen, ceruminous
cerat- (G) -- same as **kerat** -- horn -- ceratin, cerato-, Ceratophyllus
cerebrum (L) -- brain -- cerebral, cerebro-
cervix, cervic- (L) -- neck -- c. uteri, cervical, cervico-
chaete (G) -- hair, bristle -- Chaetognatha, Oligochaeta
chalaza (G) -- sty -- chalazion, chalaxium(a)

chil- (G) -- lip -- chilognathus, Chilomastix
chilo- (G) -- lip -- chilognathouranoschisis, Chilomastix
chir- (G) -- hand -- chiropodist, chirurgeon, Chiroptera
chit- (G) -- coat -- chitin, chitoneme, chitonitis
chlamys, chlamyd- (G) -- mantle -- Chlamys, Chlamydobacteria, Chlamydomonas, chlymidospore
chlor- (G) -- green -- chlorophyll, chloragogue
chrom-, chromat- (G) -- color -- chromosome, chromatin, achromatic
-cide (L) -- kill -- germicide
cilium, -a (L) -- eyelid -- m. ciliaris, Ciliata, ciliary
circum (L) -- around -- circumcise, circumoesophageal
cis- (L) -- cut -- excise, incision
coel- (G) -- same as **celo** -- hollow -- coelom, Coelenterata
com- (L. cum) -- with, together -- commissura, commissure, commensal
communis, -e (L) -- common -- m. flexor communis
con- (L. cum) -- with -- connection
contra (L) -- against -- contralateral
cornu, -a (L) -- horn -- c. ammonis, cornea, corneum, cornucopia
corona (L) -- crown -- coronary, corolla, c. capitis, c. radiata, coronal, coronella
corpus, corpora (L) -- body -- c. luteum, corpora, quadrigemina, corpse, corpulence, corpusculum, corpuscle
cortex, cortic- -- bark -- c. ceribri, cortical, cortico-
crypt- (G) -- hidden -- crypt, cryptic, cryptogam
curr- -- (L) -- run -- current, curriculum, recurrens
cyst (G) -- bladder -- cystectomy, cysticircus, cysto-
cyt- (G) -- hollow, cell -- leucocyte, cyton, cytoplasm
de (L) -- from -- deferens; in privitive sense -- decomposition
decid- (L) -- fall -- decidua, deciduous
demi (F. from L. dimidius) -- half -- demilune, deminatured
dendron (G) -- tree -- dendraxon, dendrite, dendriform, dendrology
dens, dent- (L) -- tooth -- dental, dentine, dentinal
deorsum (L) -- downward -- deorsumduction, deorsumversion
derm-, dermat- (G) -- skin -- dermal, dermis, dermatome, pachyderm
descendens (L) -- going down -- aorta descendens
deutero- (G) -- second -- deutencephalon, deuteroplasm, deuterium
dexter, dextra, dextrum (L) -- right -- destral, dextrin, dextro-
dia (G) -- through -- dialysis, diaphragm, diarrhea
diplo- (G) -- double -- diploid, diploblastic
dis-, di- (G) -- two, double -- districhiasis, digastric
dis-, di- (L) -- apart from, asunder -- dissect, diverge
dorsum (L) -- back -- dorsal, dorsalis(e), dorso-
drilus, -i (G) -- worm, lizard -- combining form of names of worms, e.g., Megadrili, Microdrili. Also Crocodilus.
duc-, duct- (L) -- lead -- abducens, adductor, duct, reduction
durus, -a, -um (L) -- hard -- dura mater, dural, duro-, induration
dyn- (G) -- power -- dyne, dynamic, dynamo
dys (G) -- difficult, painful, ill -- dyspnea, dysgenic, dysfunction
e (L) -- from, out -- educt; also in privitive sense -- enervate
ec (G) -- out of -- ecdysis, ectopic; also for **oec**
echin- (G) -- hedgehog, spiny -- Echinodermata, echinous
ecto (G) -- out, outside -- ectoderm, ectoplasm

edaph- (G) -- soil -- edaphic, edaphology, edaphon, Edaphosaurus
ego (L) -- I -- egocentric, egomania
-ella (L) -- diminutive -- Doridella from Doris
em (G) -- in -- empyema, embryo, embolus
emys (G) -- tortoise -- prefix and suffix of names, e.g., Emysuchus, Graptemys
en (G) -- in -- encapsulate, encysted, encephalon, enzyme
enchyma (G) -- infusion -- enchymatous, parenchyma
endo (G) -- in, inside -- endoderm, endoplasm, endocrine
-ens, -iens (L. present participial ending of second and third conjugation) -- ing -- rubens (reddening), flavens (yellowing), ambiens (going around)
ent- (G) -- within -- ental, enteron, dysentery, entero-
eo- (G) -- dawn -- Eoanthropus, eocene, eolith
epi (G) -- upon, on top of -- epidermis, epinephrin, epistasis
erg- (G) -- work -- erg, ergasia, ergastoplasm, energy
erythro- (G) -- red -- erythrocyte, erythrophyl, erythrophage
eso (G) --   1. within -- esethmoid, esogastritis
          2. for oeso from oiso -- I shall carry -- esophagus
esthes- (G) -- feeling -- anesthesia, esthetic
ether (G) -- pure, upper air -- ethereal
ethm- (G) -- sieve, strainer -- ethmo-, ethmoid
ethn- (G) -- people, race -- ethnic, ethnology
etio- (G) -- cause -- etiology, etiotropic
eu (G) -- well, very, exceedingly -- Eutheria, eugenic
ex (G. and L.) -- from, out -- exostosis, excurrent
exo (G) -- outside, on outside -- exocrine, exoskeleton
externus, -a, -um (L) -- on outside -- m. obliquus externus, iliaca externa, os externum
extra (L) -- outside -- extracellular
extremus, -a, -um (L) -- last -- extremitas, extremity
fac- (L) -- make, do -- factor, facultative
facies (L) -- face -- f. anterior, facet, facio-, superficial
fascia, -ae (L) -- band, fillet -- f. lata, fasciculus (i), Fasciola
fect- (L) -- made, done -- affect, defect, effector, infect
fer- (L) -- carry -- afferens, afferent, efferens, efferent, vas deferens
fibra, -ae (L) -- fiber -- f. auriculae, ff. arciformes, fibril, fibrilla, fibrillate, fibrin, fibro-, fibroid
fin- (L) -- end -- affinity, define, infinite
fiss- (L) -- cleave -- fission, Fissipedia, fissure
flagellum -a (L) -- whip -- Flagellate, flagello-
flavus, -a, -um (L) -- yellow -- Flavobacterium, flavescent, ligamenta flava, riboflavin
flect-, flex- (L) -- bend -- reflect, flexion, flexor (es), flexura
flor (L) -- flower -- flora, floret, florid, efflorescence
flu- flux- (L) -- flow -- fluid, effluent, diffluence, fluxus
folium, -a (L) -- leaf -- f. vermis, foliaceous, foliate, Trifolium
foramen, foramina (L) -- opening -- f. magnum, ff. alveolaria, Foraminifera
form (L) -- shape -- vermiform
-formes (L) -- suffix or order names of birds and some fishes -- Passeriformes, Cypriniformes
fract- (L) -- break -- fracture, refract
-fuge (L) -- drive away -- vermifuge

fundus, -i (L) -- bottom -- f. oculi, fundal, fundic
funis, funic- (L) -- cord -- f. argenteus, funiform, funiculus (i)
fus- (L) -- pour out -- fusion, infusoria, perfuse
fusus (L) -- spindle -- Fusarium, fusiform, Fusobacterium fusiformis
-gale (G) -- weasel, martin, cat -- suffix of names of cat-like animals -- Spilogale, Boreogale; also Galeodes
gam- (G) -- marriage -- gamete, gametophyte, cryptogam, monogamy
gaster, gastr- (G) -- belly -- gasterangiemphraxis, gastro-, gastrula
ge- (G) -- earth -- geology, geotropism
gen-, geno-, -geny, genesis (G) -- bring to life, create, make -- gene, genetics, genotype, parthenogenesis, sporogenous, zymogen
genus, genera (L) -- kind, race, one of the Linnaean categories (Cf. Biological Nomenclature), generic
gest- (L) -- carry -- gestation, ingest, digest
glia (G) -- glue -- glial, gliadin, fibroglia, myoglia, neuroglia
gluc- or **glyc-** (G) -- sweet -- glucose, glycemia, glycerin
gon- (G) -- angle -- goniometer, trigone
gone- (G) -- seed, offspring -- gonad, gonepoiesis, eugonic
gram- (G) -- written -- diagram, electrocardiogram
gress-- (L) -- advance -- egress, ingress, progress
graph, -y (G) -- writing -- kymograph
gymn- (G) -- naked -- Gymnamoebida, gymnema, gymnosperm
gyn-, gynec- (G) -- woman -- gynander, gynecology
gyrus, -i (G) -- circle -- g. centralis, gyro-, Spirogyra
haem -- see **hem-**
hal- (G) -- salt -- halide, halogen
hal- (L) -- breathe -- exhale, inhale, halitosis
ham- (L) -- hook -- os hamatum, hamulus, hamular
haplo- (G) -- single, simple -- haploid
hapt- (G) -- bind, fasten -- hapten, haptophore
haust- (L) -- drinking -- haustorium, haustrum (a), haustral
hebe (G) -- youth, puberty -- hebecarpous, hebin
hecto- (G. from hekaton) -- hundred -- hectogram, hectoliter
helix- helic- (G) -- coil -- Helix, helicine, helicotrema
helminth- (G) -- worm -- Platyhelminthes, helminthology
hem- (for **haem** -- G) -- blood -- hemocytometer, hemal, hematoxylin, hemaglobin, anemia, hemelytrometra
hemi- (G) -- half, incomplete -- Hemichordata, hemiazygos, Hemiptera
hepat- (G) -- liver -- hepatic, hepatectomy
hetero- (G) -- other, different -- heterosis, h eterozygote, heterodont
hex- (G) -- six -- hexagon, hexose
herp- (G) -- creep -- Herpes, herpetic, herpetology, Herpetomonas
hiatus, -us (L. English plural -- hiatuses) -- aperture -- h. aorticus
hilum, -a or **hilus, -i** (L) -- small bit or tuft -- h. lienalis, hilitis
histo- (G) -- web, tissue -- histology, histocyte, (also h istiocyte), histogenesis
holo- (G) -- all, entire, whole -- holoblastic, holophytic, holozoic, holism
homeo- (G) -- like -- homeopath
homo- (G) -- alike -- homology, homogenize, homozygote, Homoptera
hormon- (G) -- arouse -- hormone, hormonic, hormono- and hormo-
humor (L) -- fluid -- aqueous humor, humoral
hyal- (G) -- glass -- hyaline

hydr- (G) -- water -- hydrolysis, hydrophobia, anhydrous, hydrophilic
hygr- (G) -- moist -- hygric, hygroscopic
hyo- (G) -- letter U or Y -- hyomandibular, hyoid
hyper (G) -- above, over, excessive -- hypertonic, hypertrophy
hypha-, -ae (G) -- web -- Hyphomycetes, hyphal
hypn- (G) -- sleep -- hypnosis
hypo (G) -- under, lower, deficient -- hypotonic, hypoglossal, hypostasis
hyster (G) -- womb, uterus -- hysterectomy, hysteropexy, hysteria
-iasis (G) -- signifying condition, state -- psoriasis
iatro- (G) -- physician -- iatrochemistry, iatric
ichthy- (G) -- fish -- Ichthyornis, ichthyology, Icelichthys
ideo- (G) -- relating to mental image -- ideometabolism, ideomotor
idio- (G) -- one's own, private, peculiar -- idiosyncrasy, idiot
im-- (L) -- not -- immature; for **in** -- in, into -- impinge
in- (L) -- not -- innominate; in, into -- incision, injection
incis- (L) -- cut into -- incision, incisor, incisura (notch)
inferior, -ius (L) -- beneath, lower -- vena cava inferior
infra (L) -- below -- infraorbital
ino -- combining form from G. **is, inos** -- sinew -- relating to fibrous tissue -- inoblast, inocyte, inogenesis
instar (L) -- image, like -- form of an insect at various stadia of metamorphosis
inter (L) -- between -- intercellular
intermedius, -a, -um (L) -- middle -- m. vastus intermedius
internus, -a, -um (L) -- inside -- m. obturator internus, carotis interna, os internum
intra (L) -- within, inside -- intracellular
intro (L) -- within -- introspection
ipsi (L) -- self -- ipsilateral
-ise see **ize**
iso- (G) -- equal -- isotonic, isosmotic, isomer, anisogamy
-issimus, -a, -um (L) -- superlative form. Cf. Agreement of Adjectives
-ite (G. **-ites, -itis**) -- 1) division of body -- somite; 2) salt or ester of an -ous acid -- sulphite
-ites (G) -- suffix denoting pertaining to -- ascites; fossil form -- Ammonites
-itis (G) -- suffix denoting inflammation -- appendicitis
-ize (G) -- denominative verb form used as suffix -- catheterize, anaesthetize. Also spelled **ise**
jac-, jact-, ject- (L) -- throw -- ejaculation, jactation, project
jug- (L) -- yoke -- jugal, jugular, conjugate, conjugation
junct- (L) -- join -- junction, conjunctive
karyo- (G) -- same as **caryo** -- nut nucleus -- karyon, karyokinesis
kele- (G) -- tumor -- keloid or cheloid, **kelo-** -- but may be from **kelis**
kelis (G) -- stain, spot, blemish -- celidosis
kerat- (G) -- horn -- keratin, keratohyalin
kilo- (G. from **chilioi**) -- thousand -- kilogram, kilometer
kin-, kine- (G) -- movement -- kinaesthetic, kinase, kinesiology, kinetics, cholecystikinin
laevo- (L) -- also **levo** -- left -- laevorotatory
lamella, -ae (L. diminutive of **lamina**) -- thin plate -- concentric -- triangular 1.
lamina, -ae (L) -- plate -- l. terminalis, laminar, Laminaria
lapara (G) -- loins or abdomen in general -- laparectomy, laparatomy

laps- (L) -- fall -- lapse, prolapse, relapsing
lateralis, -e (L) -- pertaining to the side -- fasciculus lateralis
latus, -a, -um (L) -- broad -- fascia lata
lav- (L) -- wash -- lavage, lavatory
leuc- (G) -- white -- leucocyte, leucopenia, leucemia
lev- (L) -- raise -- levate, levator, lever
levo- (L) -- left -- levorotation, levulose
lig- (L) -- bind -- ligament, ligature
limen, limin- (L) -- threshold -- l. nasi, liminal
lipo- (G) -- fat -- lipase, lipid, lipin, lipo-, lipoid
liquor, -es (L) -- liquid, fluid -- l. folliculi
lith- (G) -- stone -- litharge, lithium, lithopedion, lithotomy
lobus, -i (L) -- lobe -- lobar, lobate, lobule, lobulus
locus, -i (L) -- place -- l. caeruleus, local, locate, locule
-log, -logy (G) -- word, study, doctrine -- analog(ue), biology, homologous
longus, -a, -um (L) -- long -- caput longum
luc- (L) -- light -- luciferase, luciferin, lucotherapy
lumbus, -i (L) -- loin -- lumbago, lumbar, lumbo-
lumen, lumina (L) -- light, window -- L. intestini, luminal
luteus, -a, -um (L) -- yellow -- c. luteum, luteal, lutein
lymph- (L) -- water -- lymphatic, lympho-, lymphoid
-ma, mata -- (G) -- indicating the result of an action -- empyema, traumatic
macro- (G) -- large -- macrocyte, macrophage, macronucleus
macula (L) -- spot -- m. albida, m. lutea, macular, maculo-
magnus, -a, -um (L) -- great, large -- foramen magnum
major, majus (L) -- greater, larger -- m. pectoralis major, os multangulum majus
mal- (L) -- bad -- maladjustment, from Fr. grand and petit mal (epilepsy); from It. malaria (bad air)
mala (L) -- cheek -- malar, malo-
malac- (G) -- soft -- malacology, Malacostraca
mamma (L) -- breast -- mammal, mammary, Mamaster, mammillary
manus (L) -- hand -- manipulate, manual, manubrium, Manulea
mas, mar- (L) -- male -- marital, dim. masculus, masculine, emasculate
mast- (G) -- breast -- mastitis, mastodon, mastoid
mastig- mastix (G) -- whip -- mastigophora, Chilomastix
matrix, matric- (L) -- womb, mould -- m. unguis, Matricaria
maxilla (L) -- jawbone -- Maxillaria, maxilliped, maxillo-
maximus, -a, -um (L) -- greatest, largest -- m. gluteus maximus
meatus (L) -- passage -- m. acusticus, urinarius
med- (L) -- middle -- medisect, medifrontal
medialis, -e (L) -- in the middle -- facies medialis, caput mediale
mediastinum (L) -- being in the middle -- m. ceribelli, testis
medianus, -a, -um (L) -- same as **medialis** -- nervus medianus
medium, -a (L) -- a means -- culture medium (Pl. media)
medulla (L) -- uncertain, possibly a diminutive of **medium** signifying the innermost part or marrow -- medulla oblongata, medullary
meg-, megal- (G) -- great -- megaspore, megalomania, acromegaly
mel, mell- (L) -- honey -- Melicera, melituria, mellitus
melan- (G) -- black -- melanin, melanophore
membrana (L) -- skin -- m. propria, membrane, mambrano-

men- (G) -- month -- menarche, menopause, amenorrhea, emmenin
mening-, meninx (G) -- membrane -- meninges, meningitis, meningo-
mens- (L) -- month -- menses, menstrual, menstruation
ment- (L) -- 1. from mens -- mind -- mental
                  2. from mentum -- chin -- mental, mentigerous, mento-
mer- (G) -- part -- mericarp, merispore, meroblastic, merogony, merozoite, metamere, dimerous
mes- (G) -- middle -- mesentery, mesoderm
meta (G) -- after, beyond, change or transformation -- metabolism, metamorphosis, metaphase, metencephalon, metabola -- combining form referring to type of metamorphosis
meter, metr- (G) -- measure -- thermometer, biometry
metra (G) -- uterus -- endo-, myo-, perimetrium, metro-
micro- (G) -- small -- micron (Pl. micra), micronucleus, microscope
mill- (L) -- thousand, many -- millepede, millepora, millimeter
mim- (G) -- imitate, mimesis, mimetic, Mimosa
minor, minus (L) -- lesser -- m. pectoralis minor, os multangulum minus
minimus, -a, -um (L) -- least -- nervus splanchnicus minimus, venae minimae
mio- (G) -- less, smaller -- miocene
misc- mixt- (L) -- mix -- miscegenation, miscible, mixture
mito- (G) -- thread -- mitochondria, mitosis, mitosome
mnem- mnes- (G) -- memory -- mnemonic, amnesia
mobil- (L) -- movable -- mobile, immobilize
mol- (L) -- 1. from mola -- mill, molar, molariform
                 2. from moles -- mass -- molecule, molal
moll- (G) -- soft -- mollusc, molluscum, Mollusca
mon- (G) -- one, single -- monosaccharide, monoecious
morb- (L) -- disease -- morbid, morbific, morbus
morph- (G) -- form, structure -- morphology, metamorphosis, polymorpho -- nuclear, amorphous
mort- (L) -- death -- mortal, mortify, mortuary
mot- (L) -- movement, mover -- oculomotor, vasomotor, pilomotor
mucus (L) -- nasal secretion -- mucin, mucoid, muco-, mucosa
multi- (L) -- many -- multinucleated, multifidus, multiple
mus, mur- (L) -- mouse -- M. musculus (Cf. mys), muridae, murine
mut- (L) -- change -- mutant, mutation
mya- (L) -- mussel -- Mya, Myodora, Solenomya
myces, mycetes (G) -- fungus -- mycelium, mycology, mycosis; used both as prefix and suffix of names, e.g., Mycetozoa, Schizomycetes
myco- (G) -- mucus -- mycocyte, Mycobacteriaceae
myel- (G) -- molar tooth -- mylohyoid
mys, my- (G) -- 1) mouse -- used as prefix and suffix of names of mouselike animals, e.g., Mysateles, Geomys. Must not be confused with **emys** (q.v.)   2) muscle (from mouse shape) -- endo-, peri-, epimysium, myasthenia, myalgia. Usually in form of **myo**: myology, myocardium, myotome, myomere, myometrium
myx- (G) -- slime, mucus -- Myxinoidei, myxedema, Myxomycetes
nan- (G) -- dwarf -- Nana, nanism, nano-, nanoid
narc- (G) -- numbness -- narco-, narcosis, narcotic
nas (L) -- nose -- nasal, nason, naso-

nat- (L) -- born -- natal, innate
nav- (L) -- boat -- navicula, f. navicularis, navi-
necro- (G) -- dead -- necrosis, necrotic
nema, nemat- (G) -- thread -- Nemathelminthes, nematocyst, nematode
neo- (G) -- new, recent -- neopallium, neoplasm
nephros, -oi (G) -- kidney -- nephridium, nephro-, epinephrin
neuron (G) -- nerve -- neural, -neurium, neuro-
neutr- (L) -- neither -- neutrocyte, neutron, neutrophil
noc- (L) -- injure -- nociceptive, nociperception, innocuous
noct- (L) -- night -- noctambulation, nocturnal, Noctiluca
nod- (L) -- knot -- nodal, node, nodose, nodule, nodus
nom- (G) -- law -- taxonomy, autonomic
nomen, nomin- (L) -- name -- nomenclature, innominate, binomial
non (L) -- not -- non-disjunction, nonelectrolyte, nonconductor
norma, -ae (L) -- carpenter-s square, pattern -- n. anterior, normal, normo-
noso- (G) -- disease -- nosencephalus, nosetiology, Nosopsyllus
noto- (G) -- back -- notochord, Notomelus
nuc- (L) -- nut -- nucellus, nucin, nucleo-, nucleus
nutr- (L) -- nourish -- nutrient, nutrition
nymph -- bride -- nympha, nymphomania
nyct- (G) -- night -- nyctalbuminaria, Nyctotherus, nycturia
ob -- (L) -- before, in front of, against -- obstruction, oblique, obstetrics
oc- (L) -- combining form of ob -- occiput, occlude, occult
oculo- (L) -- eye -- oculofacial, oculomotor, ocular
odont- (G) -- tooth -- odontology, homodont, odontoblast
odyn- (G) -- pain -- anodyne, -dynia
oec-, ec- (G) -- house -- dioecious, ecology, economy
oeso -- see **eso**
-oid (G) -- like -- neuroid, toxoid
-ole (from **olus** L) -- diminutive -- arteriole, centriole
oleum (L) -- oil -- olefiant, oleic, oleo-
olfac- (L) -- smell -- olfaction, olfactory
oligo- (G) -- few -- oligodendroglia, oligodynamic
-oma (G) -- suffix indicating pathological condition -- carcinoma, dermatoma
omentum (L. corruption of operimentum -- covering) -- omental, bursa
    omentalis, omento-
omnis, -e (L) -- all -- omnivora omnivorous, omnopon
omo- (G) -- shoulder -- omitis, omohyoid
omphalo- (G) -- navel -- omphalomesenteric, exompholos
onco- (G) -- barb, tumor -- Oncocera, oncology, oncosis
ont- (G) -- being -- paleontology, ontogeny
onyx, onych- (G) -- claw, nail -- Trionyx, Onychiurus, Stylonychia, ony-
    chophora, eponychium
oön (G) -- egg -- ootheca, cumulus oöphorus
ophis (G) -- snake -- ophiasis, Ophidia
ophthalmo- (G) -- eye -- ophthalmoscope
opisth- (G) -- behind, at the back -- opisthocoelus, opisthotic, Opisthocosmia
ops, opic- (G) -- eye -- nycatalops, -opia, -opic, -optic
opsis (G) -- sight, appearance -- suffix to names of animals signifying
    similarity to another animal -- Doridopsis, similar to Doris
opson (G) -- sauce, seasoning -- opsonin, opsonic

optimus, -a, -um (L) -- best -- optimum temperature
or- see **os, or-**
orb- (L) -- circle -- orbicular, orbit, orbito-
orch- (G) -- testicle -- orchectomy, orchiditis, orchio- mesorchium
ornis, ornith- (G) -- bird -- Alcippornis, ornithology, Neo-ornithes
orrho- (G) -- whey, blood serum -- orrhodiagnosis, orrhotherapy
ortho- (G) -- straight -- orthogenesis, Orthoptera, orthopedist
os, or- (L) -- mouth -- os uteri internum and externum, rima oris, oral
os, oss- (L) -- bone -- os cordis, os innominatum, alae magnae ossis sphenoidalis, ossa cuneiformia
-osis (G) -- denoting a condition -- leucocytosis, dermatomycosis
osm- (G) -- smell -- osmatic, osmesis, osmium, osmology
osmo- (G) -- pushing -- osmose, osmosis, osmotic
osteo- (G) -- bone -- osteology, Teleostei
ostium -a (L) -- mouth, opening -- ostium tubae abdominale, ostia of crayfish heart
ot- (G) -- ear -- otalgia, otic, otology
ovalis, -e (L) -- egg-shaped, oval -- fossa ovalis, foramen ovale
ovum (L) -- egg -- oviduct, ovarian
oxus, oxy- (G) -- sharp, pointed -- Amphioxus, oxygen, Oxyura
pachy- (G) -- thick -- pachyderm
paed- (G) -- child -- paedogenesis
pagus (G) -- fasten together, twin monster -- first element of word indicates point of attachment, e.g., pygopagus
paleo- (G) -- old -- paleontology, paleocene
palin- (G) -- again, back -- palingenesis
palp- (L) -- to feel -- palp, palpate, palpato-
palbebra, -ae (L) -- eyelid -- m. palpebrae superioris, palpebral
pan, pant- (G) -- all -- panspermy, pangenesis, pantothenic
papilla, -ae (L) -- nipple -- papillary, papilliform, papillo-
par (L) -- pair, even -- p. nonum, p. vagum, impar (uneven)
par- (L) -- bring forth -- nullipara, primipara, oviparous
para (G) -- beside, near, wrong in -- parathyroid, parachordal, Paranoia; com bining form of names denoting close relationship to principal form, e.g., Parapeneus
paries, pariet- (L) -- wall -- p. carotica, parietal, Parietaria
pars, part- (L) -- part -- p. intermedia, partial, particulate
part- (L) -- giving birth -- parturition, partus
parthen- (G) -- virgin -- parthenogenesis
pat- (L) -- lie open -- patency, patent
path-, pathy- (G) -- suffer, pain -- pathology, sympathetic
pauro- (G) -- little, few -- combining form of names denoting fewness of some structure, e.g., Pauropoda
pecilo- -- see **poikilo**
pecten (G) -- comb -- pectenate, pectineal, m. pectineus
pectus, pector- (L) -- chest, breast -- pectoral, expectorate
ped- (L) -- foot -- pedicel or pedicle, peduncle, biped
pellic- (L) -- dim. of pellis -- skin -- pellicle, pellicular
ped- (G) -- same as **paed-** -- child -- pediatrics, pedagogue
penia (G) -- poverty, reduced amount -- leucopenia
pent- (G) -- five -- pentad, pentane, Pentosoma, pentose

peps-, pept- (G) -- digest -- pepsin, peptic, pepto-
per (L) -- through -- perfuse, permeable, peroxide
peri (G) -- around -- periosteum, pericardum, perineurium, perimetrium
petr- (G) -- rock -- petroleum, petrosal, petrous
phag- (G) -- devour -- phagocytosis, bacteriophage, anthropophage
phalanx, phalang- (G) -- line of soldiers -- Phalanger, phalanges
phall- (G) -- penis -- phalli-, phallic, phallo-, phallus
phaner- (G) -- visible, manifest -- Phanerogam, phaneroscope
pharmac- (G) -- drug -- pharmaceutical, pharmacist, pharmacology
phase (G) -- appearance -- one of the stages of development, e.g., metaphase;
    a distinct portion of a heterogeneous system, e.g., oil and water
phasis (G) -- speech -- aphasia, heterophasia
pheme or phemy (G) -- speech -- heterophemia or heterophemy
pheno- (G) -- appearance -- phenotype, phenology, phenomenon(a)
-phil- (G) -- loving -- eosinophil, hydrophil, hemophilia, philanthropy
phleb- (G) -- vein -- phlebitis, phlebotomy
phlo- (G) -- bark of tree -- phloem, phlorizin
-phob (G) -- hating -- hydrophobe, hydrophobia, Helophobius
phon- (G) -- voice -- phonation, phonetic, phonophore, Phelerophonia
phor- (G) -- bearing -- phorocyte, cataphoresis, melanophore
phos (G) -- light -- phose, phosgene, phosphorus
photo- (G) -- light -- photosynthesis, photoscopic
phren- -- (G) -- 1) diaphragm -- phrenic; 2) mind -- phrenology, aphrenia
phy- (G) -- produce -- diphyodont, monophyodont, Xenophya
phylax-, phylac- (G) -- protector -- anaphylaxis, phylacogic
phyco- (G) -- seaweed -- phycochrome, Phycomycetes
phyl- (G) -- tribe, race -- phylum, phylogeny, phyletic
phyll- (G) -- leaf -- phyllotaxis, chlorophyll
physal- (G) bladder -- Physalia, physaliphore, Physaloptera
physi- (G) -- 1) nature, constitution -- physics, physiology, physique;
    2) growth -- epiphysis, hypophysis, apophysis
phyt- (G) -- plant -- phytopathology, Thallophyta, saprophytic
picr- (G) -- bitter -- Picraena, picric, picro-
pilus, -i (L) -- hair -- pilar, Pilocarpus, arrector pili
pinna, -ae (L) -- feather, wing -- pinnate, Pinnotheres, bipinnaria
pituit- (L) -- phlegm -- pituitary, pituicyte, pituitrin
planus, -a, -um (L) -- flat -- Planaria, plane, plani-, plano-, planula
plasm-, plasmat- (G) -- anything formed or moulded -- protoplasm, plasma,
    plasmo-, Plasmodium
plast- (G) -- relating to plasm -- chloroplast, plastic, plastid
platy- -- flat -- Platyhelminthes, Platypus, amphiplatyan
pleg- (G) -- stroke -- hemiplegia, gastroplegia
pleo- (G) -- more -- pleomorphism, pleonasm, pleochromatic
pleio- (G) -- more -- pleiocene, pleiotropia
pleist- (G) -- most -- pleistocene
plesio- (G) -- near -- plesiomorphism, Plesiosaurus
pleur- (G) -- side -- pleura, pleural, pleurisy, somatopleure
plexus, -us (L) -- Eng. Pl. plexuses -- network -- plexus nervosus,
    venosus, lymphaticus
plica (L) -- fold -- plica semilunaris, plicate, plication
pluma, -ae (L) -- feather -- plumose, plumule

plur- (L) -- many -- pluriceptor, pluriglandular
pne- (G) -- breathe -- pneograph, apnea, eupnea, Enteropneusta
pneuma, pneumat- (G) -- breath, air -- pneumatic, pneumon (lung)
pod- (G) -- foot -- pseudopod, pseuodpodium, Cephalopod(a)
polesis (G) -- making -- hemopoiesis, erythropoietic
poikilo- (G) -- manifold -- poikilothermous, poikilocyte
polio- (G) -- gray -- poliomyelitis, polioplasm, poliosis
poly- (G) -- many -- polybasic, polychromatic, polymer, polymorphic, polyp.
   (poly and pous -- foot). Combining form of names, meaning many
   of some structure, e.g., Polyodontidae
pons, pont- (L) -- bridge -- p. Varolii, pontal, pontine, ponticulus, ponto-
poro- (G) -- pore -- porencephaly, Porifera, poro-
porta (L) -- gate -- p. hepatis, portal
posit- (L) -- placed -- position, suppositorium
post- (L) -- after, behind -- postcaval, postcentral, postdural
posterior, -ius (L) -- behind -- posterior vena cava, tuberculum posterius
postero- (L. combining form of **posterus** -- behind) -- posterolateral
poten- (L) -- power -- potency, potential, impotence
praxis (G) -- a doing -- Praxithea, eupraxia
prae (L) -- same as **pre**
pre- (L) -- before -- prenatal, precaval
press- (L) -- pressed -- presso-, pressor, pressure, depress, suppress
prim- (L) -- first -- primary, Primates, primipara
privus -- (L) -- deprived of -- privus, privic
pro (L) -- in front of -- process, prolabium
pro (G) -- before -- prophase, pronephros, prostate
pro (G) -- before -- prophase, pronephros
procto- (G) -- anus -- proctodaeum, proctology, enteroproctia
proso- (G) -- forward -- prosocele, prosogaster, prosopagus
prosopo- (G) face -- prosopalgia, Prosopium, Platyprosopos
profundus, -a, -um (L) -- deep -- m. flexor digitorum profundus, arteria
   profunda
pronus, -a, -um (L) -- turned forward, bending down -- m. pronator teres, prone
proprius, -a, -um (L) -- own, proper -- m. extensor digiti quinti proprius,
   proprioceptive
prote- (G. Proteus, a god who could change his form at will) -- protean,
   Proteo -- combining form of names denoting changeable shape, e.g.,
   Proteomyxa, Proteosoma
proto- (G) -- first, primitive -- protoplasm, protein, protozoa
proximus, -a, -um (L) -- nearest -- proximal, proximad, proximoataxia
pseud- (G) -- false -- pseudopod, pseudostratified, combining form of names
   signifying not true form, e.g., Pseudopallene
psyche (G) -- mind -- psychic, psychobiology, psychopathic, psychosis
pter-, ptery-, pteryx, pterid- (G) -- wing pterygold, Pteridophyta, Crossop-
   terygii., Pterodactyl, Archeopteryx
-ptera -- suffix denoting type of wing of many orders of insects, e.g., Diptera;
   also the winged mammals, Chiroptera
pthisis (G) -- a wasting disease -- gastropthisis
ptosis- (G) -- falling -- p. adiposa, -ptosia, Ptosima
ptyxis (G) -- fold -- gastroptyxis, Ptychemys, Ptychodes
pubes, -is (L) -- the signs of puberty, youth -- os pubis, pubic, pubofemoral
pulmo, pulmon- (L) -- lung -- pulmotor, pulmonary, pulmocutaneous

puls- (L) -- to push on -- pulsate, pulse, pulsus, pulsellum
pulv-, pulver- (L) -- powder -- pulvis, pulverize, pulverulent
punct- (L) -- dot, point -- punctate, punctiform, punctum, punctura
pus, pur- (L) -- pus -- purulent, suppuration, pustule
putr- (L) -- rotten -- putrefaction, putrescent, putrid
py-, pyo- (G) -- pus -- pyemia, pyogenic, Pyococcus, pyorrhea
pycn- (G) --thick, dense -- pycnidium, pycnotic
pyel- (G) -- pan, pelvis -- pyelitis, pyelogram
pyg- (G) -- buttocks -- pygalgia, Pygopodes, cytopyge, steatopygous
pyl- (G) -- gate -- pylar, pyle, pylic, pylorus, Dipylidium
pyr- (G)-- fire -- pyrexis, pyrogenic, pyromania, pyrophobia
pyri- or **piri-** (L) -- pear -- m. pyriformis or piriformis, pyriform or piriform
quadr- (L) -- four-fold -- quadriceps, quadruped, quadrivalent
qual- (L) -- of what kind? -- qualimeter, qualitative
quant- (L) -- how much? -- quantivalence, quantum
quart- (L) -- fourth -- quartan, quarter, quarto-
quinque (L) -- five -- quinquetubercular, quinque- or quinquivalent
quint- (L) -- fifth -- quintessence, quinti-, quintuplet
quot (L) -- how many? -- quota, quotidian, quotient, aliquot
racem- (L) -- bunch of grapes -- raceme, racemic, racemose
radi- (L) -- ray, spoke of a wheel -- radiation, radioactivity, Radiolaria, radius
radix, -ces -- (L) -- root(s) -- radix aortae, radical, radicle
ramus, -i (L) -- branch -- ramus communicans, rami inferiores, ramify
raphe (G) -- seam -- raphe, anococcygea, raphe scroti
-raphy (G) -- suturing, stitching -- cardiorrhaphy
re- (L) -- back, again -- regenerate, react, reagent, receptor
recess- (L) -- small hollow, withdrawing -- recessus opticus, recessive
recto- (L) -- combining form of **rectum** -- rectoscope, rectovesical
rectus, -a, -um (L) -- straight, right -- m. rectus abdominis, arteriolae rectae, rectum (intestinum)
ren (G) -- kidney -- r. mobilis, renaden, renal, reni-, reno-
rete, -ia (L) -- net -- rete testis, retiform, retina
reticulum, -a (L) -- diminutive of rete -- reticular, reticulocyte
retro (L) -- behind -- retroperitoneal, retroversion
rhabd- (G) -- rod -- Rhabditis, rhabdoid, Rhabdomonas
rhach- (G) -- spine -- rhachial, rhachitis, rhachio-
rhag- (G) -- burst -- hemorrhage
rhe- (G) -- flow -- rheobase, rheotropism; when preceded by a short vowel another *r* added: diarrhea, catarrh, hemorrhoids
rheum- (G) -- watery discharge -- rheumatism, rheumatoid, rheumic
rhex- (G) -- rupture -- cardiorhexis
rhis- rhin- (G) -- nose -- rhinoceros, rhinencephalon
rhiz- (G) -- root -- rhizome, mycorrhiza, Rhizopoda
rhod- (G) -- rose -- rhododendron, rhodopsin
rhysis (G) -- a flowing -- eudiemorrhysis
rima (L) -- slit -- r. oris, rimose, rimula
rot- (L) -- turn, wheel -- rotator, rotula
rub-, rubr- (L) -- red -- rubedo, rubeola, rubin, Rubus, rubro-
ruga, -ae (L) -- wrinkle, fold -- r. gastrica, rugose, rugosity
rupt- (L) -- break -- rupture, erupt, disrupt
sacc- (L) -- sac -- saccate, sacciform

sacchar- (G) -- sugar -- saccharide, saccharin, Saccharomyces
sacrum (L) -- sacred -- os sacrum, sacroiliac
sal, salis (L) -- salt -- sal ammoniac, saline
salpinx, salping- (G) -- trumpet -- the Fallopian and Eustachian tubes, salpingitis, salpingocyesis
sangui- (L) -- blood -- sanguinary, sanguine
sanitas (L) -- health -- sanitation, sanitary, sanity, sanitarium
sanus-, -a, -um -- healthy -- sane, "mens sana in corpore sano" -- "a sound mind in a healthy body," sanity
sapo, sapon- (L) -- soap -- s. viridis, saponify
sapr- (G) -- rotten -- sapremia, saprine, saprophyte, saprozoic
sarx, sarc- (G) -- flesh -- Sarcodina, sarcoma, sarcomere, sarcoplasm, sarcostyle
scala, -ae (L) -- stairway -- s. tympani, scale
scalen- (G) -- uneven -- scalene, m. scalenus
scapula, -ae (L) -- shoulder-blade -- s. alata, scapular, scapulo-
scat- (G) -- excrement -- scatemia, scato-, scatol, scatology
scend-, scensc- (L) -- climb -- ascendens, descendens, descensus
scaph- (G) -- skiff -- scaphocephalic, scaphoid
schisto- (G) -- split, cleaved -- schistocyte, Schistosoma
schiz- (G) -- split, cleave -- schizaxon, Schizomycetes, schizophrenia
sciss- (L) -- cut, cleave -- scission, scissors, scissura
scler- (G) -- hard -- sclera, sclerectomy, sclerosis, sclerotome
scolex, scolec- (G) -- worm -- scoleciform, scolecoid
scolio- (G) -- curved -- scoliometer, scoliosis
scop- (G) -- to see -- scopophobia, microscope
scoto- (G) -- darkness -- scotodinia, scotoma, scotopic
scutum, -a (L) -- shield -- scute, Scutellaria, scutellum, scutiform, scutulum
scyph- (G) -- cup -- Schyphanthus, scyphiform, Chenendroscyphia
sebum (L) -- suet -- sebaceous, sebiferous, sebiparous, seborrhea
secret- (L) -- separated -- secrete, secretion, secretagogue
sect- (L) -- cut -- section, sectorial, insect, dissect
secundus, -a, -um (L) -- second -- secundae viae, secundina, secundipara
sed-, sess- (L) -- sit -- sedentary, sediment, sessile
semen, semin- (L) -- seed -- seminal, seminiferous
semi- (L) -- half -- semilunar, m. semimembranosus
sen- (L) -- old -- senescent, senile
sens- (L) -- perception -- sensation, sense, sensorimotor, sensory
sent- (L) -- feel -- sentient, sentiment
sepsis, septic- (G) -- putrefaction, rotting, infection -- antisepsis, septicemia
sept- (L) -- seven -- septan, septemlineatus
septum, -a (L) -- fence, barrier -- septate, septomarginal, septulum(a)
sequ- (L) -- follow -- sequel, sequela, -ae
sequest- (L) -- lay aside -- sequester, sequestrum
serra (L) -- saw -- serrate, Serratia, m. serratus
serum, -a (L) -- whey, watery part -- serine, serum, serology, serosa
sesemo- (G) -- seed of sesame plant -- sesemoid
sesqui- (L) -- one and a half -- sesquioxide
sessile (L) -- sedentary, low, dwarf
seta, -ae (L) -- hair, bristle -- setaceous, Setaria, setiferous
sex (L) -- 1. six -- sexdigitate, sexvalent
2. from sexus -- sex -- sexology, sexual

sext- (L) -- sixth -- sextan, sextivalent, sextipara
sial- (G) -- saliva -- sialaden, sialagogue, sialorrhea
sicc- (L) -- dry -- siccant, sicco-, dessicate
sider- (G) -- iron -- siderism, siderophil, siderosis
sigma (G) -- letter s -- sigma reaction, sigmoid flexure
signum, -a (L) -- sign -- signa, signature, signaturist
silic- (L) -- flint -- silica, silliceous, Sillicoflagellida, silicon
similis, -e, -ia (L) -- like -- similia similibus curantur (likes are cured by
      likes), similimum or simillimum
simul (L) --   1. at the same time -- simultaneous, simultaneity
                   2. imitate, feign -- simulation, Simulepsis, Simulium
sinister, sinistra, -um (L) -- left, of bad import -- sinistral, sinistrose,
      sinistrocardial
sinus, -us (L. English plural, sinuses)) -- bay, hollow -- sinusitis, sinusoid
sito- (G) -- food -- sitology, sitotoxin, sitotropism, parasite
situs, -us (L) -- place, site -- s. inversus, in situ ("as is")
skat- -- see **scat**
skelet- (G) -- dry -- skeletal, skeleto-, skeleton(a)
skia (G) -- shadow -- skiagram, skiascopy, skiodan
sol (L) --   1. sun -- solar, solarium, solarize, Solaster
                 2. from solvere -- to loosen -- solation, solute, solution
solen (G) -- pipe, channel -- solenitis, solenoid, solenocyte, Solenaria, Leuco-
      solenia, typhlosole
solv- (L) -- loosen -- solvation, solvent, dissolve
soma, somat- (G) -- body -- somatic, somatology, somatoplasm, somatopleure,
      somite, chromosome
somn- (L) -- sleep -- somnambulism, somnolence
son- (L) -- sound -- sonifer, sonitus, sonometer
soph- (G) -- wise -- Sophia, sophisticate, philosophy
sopor -- (L) -- stupor -- soporific, soporose, soporous
sorb- (L) -- suck up -- absorb, resorbin, Sanguisorba
spad- (G) -- rent -- epispadias, hypospadias
spec- (L) -- look at -- specillum, spectacle, speculum
species (L sing. and pl.) -- kind, sort -- special, specific
spectrum, a- (L) -- appearance, image -- spectrography, spectroscope
sperm-, spermat- (G) -- seed -- sperm-aster, spermatic, spermatid, spermato-
      cyte, Spermatophyta, spermatozoon (a), spermatozoid
sphag- (G) -- throat -- sphagiasmus, sphagitis, esophagus
sphen- (G) -- wedge -- sphenoid, sphenopalatine, sphenotic
sphincter (G) -- that which binds, band -- pyloric s., s. pupilae, sphincteroscope
sphygmo- (G) -- pulse -- sphygmograph, sphygmomanometer, asphyxia
spica (L) -- ear of grain -- s. nardi, spicula, spicule, spiculum (a)
spina (L) -- thorn -- s. bifida, spinal, spinalis, spinocortical
spir- (L) -- breathe -- spirometer, expire, inspiration, respiratory
spir- (G) -- coil -- spireme, Spirochaeta, Spironema
spirillum, -a (L) -- little coil -- Spirillaceae, spirillosis
spiritus, -us (L) -- breath, soul -- spirit, s. frumenti
splanch- (G) -- internal organs -- splanchnic, splanchnopleure
splen (G) -- spleen -- splenectomy, spleniform, splenocyte
spleni- (G) -- bandage -- spenial, m. splenius, splenium
spondyl- (G) -- vertebra -- spondylarthritis, spondylosis, spondylous

spor- (G) -- seed -- sporangium, spore, sporogeny, Sporozoa
squam- (L) -- scale -- squama, squamate, squamosal, squamous
stadium, -a (G) -- measure -- stage of disease, interval in metapmorphosis
stalagm- (G) -- a dropping -- stalagmite, stalagmometer, Stalagmopygus
stamen, stamin- (L) -- warp of loom, thread -- stamina, staminode, staminiferous
stapes, staped- (L) -- stirrup -- stapedial, m. stapedius
staphyl- (G) --bunch of grapes, the uvula -- staphylitis, Staphylococcus
stasis, stat- (G) -- standing still -- hemostasis, hemostat, static
status (L) -- state, condition -- s. epilepticus, statuvolence
stear-, steat- (G) -- fat -- steapsin, stearin, steatopygous
stech- -- see **stoich-**
stella, -ae (L) -- star -- s. lentis, Stellacantha, stellate, stellula
stem- (G) -- sheath of phallus, stamen -- stemodia, diplosteminous, Trichostema
sten- (G) -- narrow -- stenion, stenopeic, stenosis
sterc- (L) -- exrement -- stercobilin, stercoral, Sterculia
stereo- (G) -- solid -- stereocilium, stereoisomer, stereoscope
steril- (L) -- sterile -- sterility, sterilization
sternum (G) -- chest -- sternebra, sternocleidomastoid
stetho- (G) -- chest -- stethemia, stethograph, stethoscope
sthen- (G) -- force, strength -- sthenia, Sthenomeris, Sthenoprya
stich- (G) -- row of things -- Stichaster, stichochrome, -stichous
stigma, stigmat- -- (G) -- mark -- astigmatism, stigmatic, stigmatodermia
stimulus, -i (L) -- goad -- stimulant, stimulate, stimulin
stirp- (L) -- stem -- sterpiculture, exstirpate
stolch- (G) -- element -- stoichiology or stoechiology or stechiology, stoichio-
  metry
stoma, stomata, -stomy (G) -- mouth -- stomodaeum, enterostomy
stratum, -a (L) -- layer -- s. lucidum, stratified, stratiform
strepto- (G) -- twisted, curved -- strepticemia, Streptococcus, Streptothrix,
  streptotrichal
stria, -ae (L) -- channel, furrow -- acoustic stria, dentinal striae, striated,
  striation, corpus striatum, striocellular
stroma, stromat- (G) -- bed -- stromal, stromatic
strongyl- (G) -- round -- Strongyloidea, strongyloplasm, Strongylus
styl- (G) -- pillar, beam -- style, styliform, styloid, stylus
sub (L) -- under -- subacetate, subconscious, subintestinal, subphylum
sublimis, -e (L) -- high, upper -- m. flexor digitorum sublimis, sublimate
succus, -i (L) -- juice -- s. entericus, s. gastricus
suct- (L) -- suck -- suction, Suctoria, suctorial
sudor (L) -- sweat -- sudation, sudorial, suderiferous, exsudate
sulcus, -i (L) -- furrow, ditch -- sulcal, sulciform, sulcomarginal
sup- (L) -- combining form of sub -- under -- suppository, suppurate
super (L) -- above -- superciliary, superdural, superficial
superficialls, -e (L) -- on the surface -- fascia superficialis
superficies (L) -- outer surface of any part
superior, -ius (L) -- upper, higher -- vena cava superior
supinus, -a, -um (L) -- on the back -- supination, supinator
supra (L) -- above -- m. supraspinatus, supracondyle, suprarenal
sur (Fr. from L. super) -- above -- surangular, surrenal
sursum (L) -- upward -- sursumduction, sursumversion
sus- (L) -- combining form of sub -- under -- suscitate, suspecta, suspensoid,
  sustentacular

sutura, -ae (L) -- a seam -- s. coronalis, suturation, suture
sym or **syn** (G) -- together -- symbiosis, symphysis, syncytium, synapse, synthesis
syrinx, syring- (G) -- pipe, tube -- Syringa, syringe, syringomyelia
sys- (G) -- combining form of syn -- together -- system, systole, syzygium
tabula, -ae (L) -- table -- tabulate, tabellae, tablature
tach-, tachy- (G) -- swift, speed -- tachometer, tachycardia
tact- (L) -- touch -- tactile, tactor, tactual, contact
taenia or **tenia** (G) -- band, tape -- t. acustica, Taenia, taeniola
talus (L) -- die -- ankle bone -- talocalcaneal
tarsus (G) -- wicker-work frame -- instep -- os tarsale, m. tarsalis, tarsotibial
taxis (G) -- arrangement, order -- phyllotaxis, taxonomy
techn- (G) -- art -- technic, technician, technocausis
techno- (G) -- child -- technotonia or technotony
techto- (G) -- builder -- techtology, techtonic, architect
tectum (L) -- roof -- t. mesencephali, tectorium, tectospinal
tegmen, tegmin- tegmentum (L) -- covering -- t. mastoideum, tegmental
tela (L) -- web -- t. aranea, t. subcutanea
tele- telo- (G) -- end, distant -- telencephalon, telephase or telophase
tempus (L) -- 1. section or division of: a) space, bounds, (temper-) -- temperament, temperance, temperature; b) time (tempor-) -- tempo, temporal, tempero;
2. the temple -- m. temporalis, temporen, temporo
ten- (G) -- tendon -- tenofibril, tenotomy, Tenontomyia
tenac- (L) -- gripping -- tenacious, tenaculum, Tenacia
tend- (L) -- stretch -- tendo, tendon, extend
tens- (L) -- stretch -- tense, tension, tensor, extension
tentorium -- (L) -- tent -- t. cerebelli, tentorial
tera-, terat- (G) -- monster -- teratism, teratology, teratosis
teres, teret- (L) -- round and long -- m. teres, 1. teres, tereti-
terg- (L) -- back -- tergal, tergo-, tergum. See **vis**
termin- (L) -- boundary, limit -- terminal, terminology, terminus
tern- (L) -- of three -- ternary, Ternidens
tert- (L) -- third -- tertian, tertiary, tertipara
testa, -ae (L) -- shell -- t. ovi, Testacea, Testudo
testis, -es (L) -- testicle -- testectomy, testibrachium, testico-
tetanus (G) -- tension -- tetanic, tetanotoxin, tetany
tetra (G) -- four -- tetrabasic, tetrad, tetravalent
text- (L) -- weave -- textiform, texture, textus
thalamus (G) -- bed, bedroom -- thalamencephalon, thalamic, thalamocortical
thallus (G) -- young shoot -- Thallophyta, thallospore
thanat- (G) -- death -- thanatognomic, thanatoid, thanatosis, euthanasia
theca, -ae (G) -- case, chest, sheath, a box -- t. folliculi, thecitis, thecodont, oötheca
thel- (G) -- nipple -- thelitis, thelium, epithelium
thely- (G) -- female -- thelyblast, thelytocia, theelin
then- (G) -- palm of hand -- thenad, thenal, thenar, thenen
ther- (G) -- wild beast -- Therapsida, Theromorpha, -therium (a) English -there(s) -- combining form of names of mammals, e.g., Eutheria, Titanotherium or Titanothere
therape- (G) -- waiting on, service, in particular, medical -- therapeusis, therapeutics, therapy

therm- (G) -- heat -- therm, thermal, thermometer, thermopile, thermos, isotherm, homothermous

thesis, thet- (G) -- a placing -- euthesis, synthesis, synthetic

thio- (G) -- sulphur -- thioacid, Thiobacillus, thiophilic

thorax, thorac- (G) -- breastplate, the chest -- thoracic, thoracolumbar

thrix, trich- (G) -- hair -- Ulothrix, Trichina, trichinosis

thrombus (G) -- clot -- thrombin, thrombogen, thrombosis

thymus (G) --   1. thyme (pronounced time) -- thymene, thymol
             2. lump, thymus gland -- thrymectomy, thymocyte
             3. mind or heart as seat of emotions -- thymopathy, -thymia

thyre- (G) -- shield -- thyreoid or thyroid, thyroxin

tibia, -ae (L) -- pipe, flute -- tibial, tibialis, -e, tibiofibula

tinct- (L) -- dye -- tinctorial, tinctura or tincture

toc- (G) -- childbirth -- tocology, tocophoral, atocia, pitocin

tome, tomy (G) -- cut -- myotome, microtome, anatomy, appendectomy

ton- (G) -- strain -- tone, tonic, tonofibril, tonus, tonodesmus, tonoplast, tonotropism, eutonon, heterotonia

top- (G) -- place -- topical, topography, atopic, ectopic

tors-, tort- (L) -- twist -- torsion, torticollis, extortor

torus (L) -- knot, swelling, bulge -- t. frontalis, torula, torulus tactilis, toric

tot- (L) -- all -- totaquina, totipotential

tox-, toxic (G) -- poison -- toxin, toxoid, intoxication

trab- (L) -- beam -- trabal, trabecula (ae), trabs cerebri

trach- (G) -- 1. rough -- trachoma, trachychromatic
             2. plus arteria -- windpipe -- trachea, tracheo-

trachel- (G) -- neck -- trachelagra, trachelion, trachelo-

tract- (L) -- draw -- tract, traction, tractus, contract, retractor

trag- (G) -- goat -- tragacanth, tragal, trago-, tragus(i)

trans (L) -- across -- transfusion, transillumination, transitional

trapez- (G) -- a table or counter -- m. trapezius, os trapezium, trapezoid

trauma, traumat- (G) -- wound -- traumatic, traumatism, traumatology

trema- (G) -- hole -- trematode, helicotrema, Haplotrema

tremo- (L) -- tremble -- tremogram, tremor, tremulor, atremia

trep- (G) -- turn -- treponema, Trepsichois, Treptichnus

treph- (G) -- nourish -- trephocyte, trephone, Zootrephes

tres-, tret- (G) -- boring -- tresus, atresia, atretic

tri- (L) -- three -- triacetate, triceps, triatomic, tricuspid, trigone

trich -- see **thrix**

trit- (L) -- rubbed -- triturate, electrolithotrity, detritus

triticum (L) -- grain of wheat -- T. vulgare, triticeo-, triticeous, corpus triticeum, cartilago triticea

troch- (G) -- wheel, disc -- troche, trochiscus(i), Trochelminthes, trochophore

trochanter (G) -- runner, head of femur -- trochanteric, trochin, trochiter

trochlea (L) -- pulley -- t. femoris, trochlear, trochlearls

trop- (G) -- turning -- tropism, geotropic, heliotrope

troph- (G) -- nourishment -- trophic, trophoblast, trophoderm, atrophy, hypertrophy, dystrophy

trud-, trus- (L) -- thrust -- intrude, intrusion, retrusion

tryptan (G) -- auger -- trypanoplasma, Trypanosoma, trepan

tryps- (G) -- rubbing -- trypsin, tryptic, tryptophan

tuba (L) -- trumpet -- t. acustica, tubage, tube, tubo-, Tubularia, tubule,
    tubulo-, tubulus(i)
tuber (L) -- swelling, knob -- t. cinereum, tubercle, tuberculosis, tuberculum,
    tuberosity
tum- (L) -- swelling -- tumefy, tumid, tumor
tunica, -ae (L) -- coat -- t. propria, Tunicata
turb- (L) -- 1. crowd -- turbid, turbidity
                  2. turned -- turbine, turbinal, turbinate, turbino-, turbo
turg- (L) -- swell -- turgescence, turgid, turgor
tyl- (G) -- lump -- tyle, tylion, tyloma, tylosis
tympanum (G) -- drum -- typanal, tympanic, n. chorda tympani, tympano-
typ- (G) -- form -- type, typic, typical, Atypena, Holectypus
typh- (G) -- smoke, cloud -- Typhaceae, Typhis, typho-, typhoid, typhus
typhlo- (G) -- blind, cecum -- typhlosis, typhlosole
tyr- (G) -- cheese -- tyrein, Tyroglyphus, tyrosine, tyrothrix
ulcus, ulcer- (L) -- ulcer -- ulcerate, ulcero-
ule (G) -- 1. scar -- ulectomy, ulerythema
                2. gum -- ulemorrhagia, ulitis, ulo-
-ule -- English form of diminutive ulus, -a, -um -- nodule, reticule
ultra (L) -- beyond -- ultrafiltration, ultramicroscope, ultraviolet
-ulus, -a, -um (L) -- diminutive suffix -- utriculus, muliercula, reticulum
umbell- (L) -- sunshade -- umbel, umbelliferous
umbo (L) -- prominence, boss -- umbilicus, umbonate
uncus (L) -- hook -- u. gyri hippocampi, unciform, uncinate
ung-, unct- (L) -- anoint -- unction, unctuous, uncture, unguent
unda (L) -- wave -- undulant, undulate, Undularia
unguis, -es (L) -- nail -- ungual, Unguiculata, unguinal
ungula, -ae -- (L) -- hoof -- Ungulata
uni- (L) -- one -- uniaxial, unicellular, unicorn, unipolar
ur- (G) -- tail -- uropod, Urochordata, Anura
ur- (G) -- urine -- urea, uremia, urine, urology, ureter, urethra
uran- (G) -- 1. Uranus, god of Heaven -- uranism, uranium
                2. roof of mouth, palate -- uranisconitis, urano-, Uranichthys
urtica (L) -- nettle -- urticaria, urticate
ust- (L) -- burnt -- Ustilago, ustulation, ustus, combustion
uter, utri- (L) -- bag -- utricular, utriculus
utero- (L) -- uterus -- uteroscope, uteroventral, uterovesical
uva (L) --   grape -- uvea, uviform, uvula, uvulo-
vaccin- (L) -- pertaining to a cow (vacca) -- vaccinate, vaccine
vacuum (L) -- empty space -- vacuole, vacuolar, vacuolate
vagina, -ae (L) -- sheath -- v. bulbi, vaginal, vagino-
vagus, -i (L) -- wandering -- n. vagus, vagal, vago-
valens, valent- (L) -- strong -- valence, -valent, valoid
vallum, -a (L) -- wall, rampart -- v. unguis, vallate, circumvallate
valv- (L) -- valve -- valvi, valvo-, valvula, valvule, valvulo-
vari- (L) -- change, spot -- variation, varicella, variola, Variolepis
varix, -ces (L) -- dilated vein -- v. anastomoticus, varicose, varico-
varus (L) -- 1. grown inwards -- talipes, varus
                  2. pimple -- v. comedo

vas, -a (L) -- vessel -- vas deferens, vasa vasorum, vascular, vaso-
veget- (L) -- to animate, enliven -- vegetal, vegetable, vegetative
velum (L) -- veil -- v. medullare, velar, veliform, velo-
vena, -ae (L) -- vein -- v. anonyma, vv. stellatae, venation, veni-, veno-
venen- (L) -- poison -- venenation, Venenosa, venom
vener- (L) -- pertaining to Venus -- venereal, venereo-, venery
venter, ventr -- (L) -- belly -- v. anterior, ventral, ventralis, -e, ventricle, ventro-
vern- (L) -- pertaining to Spring -- vernal, vernalization, vernation
vermis, -es (L) -- worm -- vermicide, vermiform, vermin
verruca (L) -- wart -- v. acuminata, veruciform, verucose, verruga
vers-, vert- (L) -- turned -- version, versicolor, vertebra, verttigo
vesica, -ae (L) -- bladder -- v. urinaria, vesical, vesicle, vesico-, vesicula, vesi-
cular
vestibulum, -a (L) -- entrance court -- vestibular, vestibule
vestig- (L) -- footstep -- vestige, vestigial, vestigium
via, -ae (L) -- way, road -- "per vias naturales" (through natural channels),
"primae viae" (first channel, i.e., alimentary tract, for getting food,
as opposed to others. Cf. segundus)
viab- (Fr. from L -- vita -- life -- and habilis -- fit) -- viability, viable
vibr- (L) -- shake -- vibrate, Vibrio, vibrissa
villus, -i (L) -- tuft of hair -- villose, villous
vin- (L) -- wine -- vinegar, vinous, vinum, vinyl
vipera (L contraction of vivipara) -- viper, snake -- Viperidae, viperine
vir (L) -- man -- virago, virile, virilism
virg- (L) -- virgin -- virginal, virginity
virt- (L) -- power, potential -- virtual, virtue, virtuous
viridis, viride (L) -- green -- viridin, viridans
virus, -i -- (L) -- poison -- virulent
vis (L) -- 1. force, energy -- "vis a tergo" (accelerating force), v. formativa, v.
vitalis
2. seen -- visible, visile, vision, visual, visus
visc- (L) -- bird lime, sticky -- viscid, viscosity, viscum
viscus, viscera (L) -- internal organ -- visceral, viscero-, eviscerate
vita, -ae (L) -- life -- vital, vitalism, vitamin, Arbor Vitae
vitell- (L) -- yolk -- vitellary, vitellin, vitello-, vitellus
vitr- (L) -- glass -- vitreo-, vitreous, vitriol, vitrina, "in vitro" (in the test
tube, as opposed to "in vivo" -- in the living animal)
viv- (L) -- alive -- vivi-diffusion, viviparous, vivisection
voc- (L) -- voice -- vocal, vocation, vociferate, provocative
vol- (L) -- 1. palm of hand -- vola, volar
2. fly -- volant, volatile
3. will -- volition, voluntary
volv- (L) -- turn -- volvulus, evolve, evolution, convolution
vomer (L) -- ploughshare -- v. cartilagineus, vomerine, vomero-
vortex, vortic- (L) -- whirlpool -- v. pilorum, Vorticella, venae vorticosae
vuln- (L) -- wound -- vulnerable, vulnerant, vulnery, vulnus
vuls- (L) -- plucked, pulled -- evulsion, convulsion, revulsent
vulva (L) -- wrapper or covering -- v. cerebri, vulval, vulvo-
xanth (G) -- yellow -- xanthein, Xanthium, xanthophyll
xer- (G) -- dry -- xerasia, xerophilic, xerophyte, xerosis
xiph- (G) -- sword -- xiphisternum, xiphocostal, xiphoid

xyl- (G) -- wood -- xylan, xylem, Xylocarpus, xylol
-yl (G from hyle) -- matter, stuff -- ethyl, vinyl
ypsill- (G) -- letter upsilon -- ypsilliform, ypsiloneura, hypsiloid
zea (G) -- fodder grain -- Z. mays, zean, zein, zeism
zeug- (G) -- yoked -- Zeugonyx, Zeuglodon, Zeugmatothrips
zona (G) -- belt -- z. radiata, zonule, zonary
zoön, zoa (G) -- living thing, animal -- zoiatria, zoic, zoögenesis, zoölogy,
   protozoa, spermatozoön (a), azoic
zym- (G) -- yeast -- zymase, zymogen, ensyme
zyg- (G) -- yoke -- zygapophysis, zygoma, zygote, azygos, homozygous, syzygy

COMMON LATIN ABBREVIATIONS AND NOMENCLATORIAL TERMS

Abbreviation	Latin Term	Meaning or Use
ascr.	ascriptum	Ascribed to
ca.	circa	About (time)
cf.	confer	Compare with
e.g.	exempli gratia	For example
emend.	emendatio	Emended
et al.	et alii	And others (persons)
f., ff.	forma formae	Form, forms
	fide	On the authority of
gen. nov.	genus novum	New genus
h.e.	hic, or hoc est	This or that is
ib., or ibid.	ibidem	The same reference
	idem	The same person
id. ac.	idem ac	The same as
i.e.,	id est	That is
in litt.	in litteris	In correspondence
	in loco	In the place
	in situ	In place
loc. cit.	loco citato	Place cited (publication and page)
n.n.; n. nov.; nom. nov.	nomen novum	New name
	nomen nudum	A name without description
	non vidi	I have not seen it
	non viso	Not seen
nov. n.	novum nomen	New name
nov. sp.	nova species	New species
op. cit.	opere citato	Publication cited (without page reference)
Q.E.D.	quod erat demonstrandum	What was to be proved
q.v.	quod vide	Which see
sc., or scil.	scilicet	Namely
seq.	sequens	Following (singular)
sqq.	sequentia	Following (plural)
	sic	Thus (exactly as transcribed)
sp.	species	Species (singular)
spp.	species	Species (plural)
sp. indet., sp. ind.	species indeterminata	Species indeterminate
sp. nov.	species nova	New species
supra cit.	supra citato	Cited above
v., or vs.	versus	Against
	vice	In place of
v., vi., vid.	vide	See
v. et.	vide etiam	See also
v.g.	verbi gratia	For example
viz.	videlicet	Namely

Origins from Mythology of Biological Names and Terms

Dr. Patrick H. Yancey, S.J.

Professor and Chairman of
Department of Biology
Spring Hill College

First Edition of the Combined Reprints
1999

Published by

William Enderle Roberts, M.D.

Reprinted under license from the
Spring Hill College Press, Mobile, AL.

Reprinted by Mississippi Printing Company, Greenwood, Mississippi

First Printing Bios XVI #5, 1944
1st Edition -- 1945   LCCN 47-15649
2nd Edition -- 1961 Third Printing

Library of Congress Catalog Card Number 99-74238

ISBN 0-9672426-0-6

ACKNOWLEDGMENTS

In the compilation of the following list of words, the author is much indebted to Jaeger's *Source-book of Biological Names and Terms*, Ziegler and Bresslau's *Zoologisches Wörterbuch*, and the *Tabulae Biologicae*. For the mythology he has consulted Hamilton's *Mythology*, Fox's *Greek and Roman Mythology*, Gayley's *Classic Myths*, and Guerber's *Myths of Greece and Rome*. He is also indebted to his students for looking up the descriptions of many of the plants and animals.

EXPLANATION

In each item of the following compilation, the mythological name is given first with a short history of the name or a synopsis of the myth connected with it. Then follows the biological names or the terms that are derived from the mythological name. Names and terms that apply to plants will be followed by (Pl); those that apply to animals will be followed by an abbreviation of the phylum, class, or order in parentheses. Since biological names are latinized, Greek names are usually given in their Latin form.

The application of the mythological name to the biological name or term is explained except in cases where the application is obvious, or where the name seems to have been chosen merely for the sake of having a name.

Origins from Mythology of Biological Names and Terms*

INTRODUCTION

To the ancients, especially to the Greeks, all nature was a manifestation of divinity. Every mountain, river, or sea was identified with some god or goddess. Every city was said to have been founded by some mythical person sooner or later deified. Every art and trade had its heavenly patron chosen because of some fabled connection of the god with that avocation. It is not surprising, then, that many plants and animals were named after gods because of some episode in the mythology of the god in which the plant or animal figured; or, contrariwise, some hero or villain was said to have been changed by the gods into a plant or animal, either as a reward or punishment, and thereafter went by the name of that natural object.

This practice of naming organisms after divinities and famous personages or from myths concerning them was continued by modern naturalists, especially those of the old school who had the benefit of a classical education and were well versed in Greek and Roman mythological lore. The shift in our education away from the classics has deprived our younger biologists of an aid in acquiring a biological vocabulary and in identifying organisms. Therefore, it has occurred to the Editor of BIOS that a short treatise on this subject might be useful for biology students; at his suggestion, the author has prepared the following list of mythological origins of biological names and terms, accompanied by as much of the mythology as he thought might be helpful and interesting.

In this regard, it must be said that in many cases there is only a remote connection between the name and the myth. For instance, many marine forms are named after sea nymphs simply because both inhabit the sea. In other cases, names seem to have been chosen merely for the sake of a name. Where this seems to be true, no explanation is given.

Since most of the myths referred to are Grecian, a few words about classical Greek concepts of the cosmos are in order. As regards the first origin of things, there was no more agreement among the Greeks than there is among modern cosmologists. According to one story, in the beginning there was only *Chaos* (nothingness) which, as Milton later described it, was " . . . the vast immeasurable abyss, Outrageous as a sea, dark, wasteful, wild." From *Chaos* were born *Nyx* (night) and *Erebus* (lower darkness). Then *Nyx* laid an egg in the bosom of *Erebus*

---

* The word "Mythology" in the title is used loosely, for the list includes the names of several historical personages of antiquity.

and from this came *Eros* (love) who created *Aether* (heavenly light) and *Hemera* (day).

Another account relates that uncreated *Nyx* existed first and, brooding over a vast abyss, laid an egg from which *Eros* came forth, the two halves of the shell becoming respectively *Uranus* (heaven) and *Gaea* (earth). They were the first parents but there is some difference of opinion about the number of their offspring. According to some they were the parents of numerous monstrous creatures such as the *Cyclopes* and the *Titans*. Others held that they had only two children: *Ocean* (the river which encircled the earth) and *Tethys* (the nurse). These, in turn, were the parents of the other *Titans* or *Elder Gods* who first ruled the earth. The most important of these were *Cronus* (Saturn) and his sister-wife, *Rhea* (Cybele). Others were: *Hyperion*, father of the son, moon, and dawn; *Mnemosyne* (memory); *Themis* (justice); and *Japetus*, father of *Atlas* and *Prometheus*.

Cronus and *Rhea* were the parents of *Zeus* (Jupiter) and *Hera* (Juno), his wife; of *Poseidon* (Neptune), god of the sea, and *Hades* (Pluto), god of the underworld; and of *Hestia* (Vesta). These children of *Cronus* and *Rhea*, together with several of the offspring of *Zeus*, such as, *Ares* (Mars), god of war; *Apollo*; *Athene* (Minerva); *Aphrodite* (Venus), goddess of love; *Hermes* (Mercury), messenger of the gods; *Artemis* (Diana); and *Rhea*'s son *Hephaestus* (Vulcan), armorer of the gods, were the *Olympians*. They overthrew *Cronus* and the *Titans* and became the rulers of the world. They dwelt on *Olympus* where they feasted on *Ambrosia* and *Nectar* and listened to *Apollo*'s music. However, they frequently descended to earth and took part in the affairs of men, especially their love affairs and wars. Thus the Trojan War, the subject of Homer's *Iliad*, was the result of the "Judgment of Paris" (q.v.) and was followed by the wanderings of *Odysseus*, described by Homer in the *Odyssey*, and of *Aeneas*, recounted by Virgil in the *Aeneid*, which connects the mythology of Rome with that of Greece. Other notable myths were "The Twelve Labors of Hercules" and "The Quest of the Golden Fleece" by Jason and the *Argonauts*.

The earth was conceived as flat and surrounded by a great river, *Ocean*, and divided in half by the *Sea* (Mediterranean and Black). Beyond *Ocean* were other mysterious lands peopled by different beings, such as the *Hyperboreans*, beyond the North Wind (Boreas), the *Ethiopians*, to the South; and the *Cimmerians*, unlocated. The *Isles of the Blessed* were also across *Ocean*.

The *Underworld* occupied a great deal of attention from the ancients. Though sometimes called *Hell*, it was not entirely a place of punishment of the wicked. Often it is referred to in its entirety as *Erebus*, which, as we have seen, was the offspring of *Chaos*. In other accounts it is divided into two parts: *Erebus*, the upper portion where the dead go immediately after death; and *Tartarus*, the lower region, usually associated with the evil spirits. It was ruled over by *Hades* and his wife *Persephone*. It had five rivers: *Acheron*, the river of woe; *Cocytus*, the river of lamentation;

Phlegethon, the river of fire; *Styx*, the river of the unbreakable oath by which the gods swore; and *Lethe*, the river of forgetfulness. *Charon* was the ferryman who carried in his boat across the *Styx* the souls of those upon whose lips had been placed the passage money. Hence the great importance of proper burial. The gate was guarded by *Cerberus*, a three-headed dog.

The origin of man was the subject of many myths. According to the Athenians, the first man was *Cecrops*, founder and first king of Athens. The Boiotians believed he was *Alkomeneus*, born from the waters of Lake Kopais as a fish. The Theban story was that men arose from dragons' teeth sown in the earth. Another attributed the creation of man to the sons of Japetus, *Epimetheus* and *Prometheus*.

A

ABDERA -- a town of Thrace. Abderites (Mam), Abderospira (Moll).

ACHATES -- friend of Aeneas, "Faithful Achates."   According to Jaeger the origin of: *Achatina* (Moll), *Achatinella* (Moll), *Achatia* (Ins). But Ziegler derives from "achates," agate, because of agate-like shell.

ACHERON -- river of woe in Hades.   *Acherontemys* (Rept), *Acherontia* (Ins).   Latter has death's head marking on body.   *Acherontiinae* (Ins).

ACHILLES -- son of Peleus and Thetis and famous Greek warrior in Trojan War.   His mother dipped him into the Styx to give him immortality. She held him by the heel which was not wet by the waters and consequently remained vulnerable.   There he was wounded. *Tendon of Achilles* by which Gastrocnemius muscle attached to calcaneus.   *Achillea* (Pl), *Achillides* (Ins), *achillein*, (alkaloid derived from *A. millefolium*).

ACHLYS -- Goddess of Obscurity.   *Achlys* (Pl), *Achlysictis* (Mam), *Achlyogegeton* (Pl).   Probably refers to habitats.

ACMENA -- a name of Venus (Pl).

ACTAEON -- a huntsman, grandson of Cadmus, turned into a stag by Artemis and killed by his own hounds.   (Moll), *Actaeonella* (Moll).   *Actaea* (Crust), *Actaeosaurus* (Rept).

ADMETUS -- King of Thessaly, to whom Apollo was indented as a servant by Zeus for having killed the Cyclopes (q.v.).   Apollo obtained a respite from death for him provided someone else would take his place.   His wife Alcestis did so but Hercules brought her back to life.   (Ins?   Jaeger derives from "admete" -- not tamed, unwedded).

ADONIS -- youth beloved by Aphrodite.   While hunting he was killed by a wild boar.   From his blood sprang the red anemone.   (Pl). *Adonidia* (Pl).

AEDON -- daughter of Pandareus, changed into a nightingale, (Av) and *Aedonopsis* (Av).

AEGYRIA -- a nymph (Ins).

AEGILOPS -- an oak (probably *Valonia*) sacred to *Zeus*.   (Pl) and (Moll). Also disease of eye in goats.

AEGINA -- a maiden beloved by Zeus and great-grandmother of Achilles. An island named after her.   (Coel), *Aeginidae* (Coel), *Aeginura* (Coel), *Aeginopsis* (Coel).

AEGISTHUS -- lover of Clytemnestra (q.v.) and, in one story, the slayer of her husband, Agamemnon (q.v.).   He, in turn, was killed by Orestes, brother of Iphigenia .   (Crust).

AENUS -- hero of Vergil's *Aeneid*.   *Anaeiides aeneus*.

AEOLIS -- daughter of Aeolus, King of the Winds, who lived on the island of Aeolia. (Moll), *Aeolagrion* (Ins), *Aeolididae* (Moll), *Aeolometris* (Ins), *Aeolomorphus* (Ins), *Aeolosoma* (Ann), *Aeolosomatidae* (Ann), *Aelus* (Ins), *Corythaeolus* (Rept). Some structure which gives impression of hair blown by the wind. Thus the gills of Aeolis. *Aeolotropism*, a response to the stimulus of wind.

AEROPE -- mother of Agamemnon. (Arach). (Moll).

AESCULAPIUS -- Latin name of Asclepios (q.v.). During a pestilence in Rome, one of the serpents of Asclepios was brought from Greece and set up in a temple in Rome and deified as the god of medicine. His wife was Hygeia (q.v.). *Erythrolamprus aesculapii* (Rept).

AESOPUS -- Greek author of fables. (Rept).

AGARISTA -- daughter of Clisthenes (Pl).

AGAVE -- daughter of Cadmus. She was driven mad by Dionysius and thought her son, Penthaeus, was a lion and killed him. (Pl) of order *Amaryllidaceae, A. americana*, Century Plant, is source of Pulque, a strong alcoholic beverage of Mexico which drives people mad.

AGDESTIS -- an hermaphrodite, descendant of Zeus and the Agde Rock (Pl).

AGLAOPHEME -- one of the Sirens (q.v.) *Aglaophenia* (Coel), *Aglaophenopsis* (Coel).

AGLAUROS -- daughter of Cecrops (q.v.). *Aglaura* (Coel), (Ann), (Ins), *Aglauridae* (Coel).

AIELLO -- one of the Harpies (q.v.) (Mam).

AJAX -- a famous Greek warrior in the Trojan War (Pl).

ALASTOR -- name of Zeus, the Avenger (Ins), (Mam).

ALCIPPE -- daughter of Area (Mars), God of War. (Av), *Alcippornis* (Av), *Alcippus* (Av). Reference to fighting quality.

ALCYONE -- wife of Ceyx, king of Thessaly, who was drowned. She grieved so much for him that she joined him in the sea and they were changed to birds. Each year for seven days ("Alcyon" or "Halcyon Days") when she broods on her nest the sea is calm. *Alcyon* (Av), *Alcyonaria* (Coel. shaped like Kingfisher's nest), *Alcyone* (Coel), *Alcyonella* (Moll), *Alcyonida* (Arthr), *Alcyonidium* (Bry), *Alcyonolithes* (Por), *Alcyonium* (Coel), *Alcyonotus* (Arthr), *Paralcyonium* (Coel), *Protoalcyonara*.

ALECTO -- one of the three Furies (Erinyes q.v.) (Echin), *Alectopes* (Mam).

ALPHAEUS -- god of the river who fell in love with Arethusa (q.v.). (Crust).

AMALTHAEA -- goat on whose milk Zeus was raised or a nymph who owned the goat. The latter is represented with a Cornucopia or Horn of Plenty. (Coel), (Moll). Cornucopia-shaped.

AMARYLLIS -- a shepherdess much referred to in pastoral poetry. (Pl), *Amaryllidaceae* (Pl).

AMBROSIA -- food of the gods. (Pl); A. artemesiaefolia, Ragweed, from flowering tops of which wormwood is made. Also certain molds used by insects for food: Ambrotodes (Ins). Ambrosioides (Pl).

AMMON -- Egyptian god identified with Zeus, represented with horns of a ram, to which reference is made. *Ammonea* (Moll), *Ammoniacum* (Pl), *Ammonicrinus* (Echin), *Ammonicerina* (Moll), *Ammonitella* (Moll), *Ammonites* (Moll). Also *ammonia*, said to have been first prepared near temple of Ammon in Lybia, and *Cornu Ammonis*, horn-shaped part of brain (hippocampus q.v.).

AMPHION -- king of Thebes, son of Zeus and Antiope (q.v.) and husband of Niobe (q.v.). He was a great musician and with his playing moved stones to Thebes which his brother, Zethus (q.v.), was fortifying. He and Zethus killed Dirce (q.v.) for mistreating their mother. (Tril). Stony.

AMPHITRITE -- wife of Poseidon (Neptune) and one of the Nereids (q.v.) (Pl.), (Ann).

AMYTIS -- daughter of Astyages. *Amytornis* (Av).

ANDROMEDA -- daughter of Cassiopeia (q.v.) condemned to be devoured by a serpent but saved by Perseus (q.v.) who married her. A constellation. (Pl), (Coel). Star-shaped.

ANEMONE -- the flower of Adonis (q.v.) (Pl), *Anemonella* (Pl), *Anemonoides* (Pl), *Anemonia* (Coel). Flower-shaped.

ANTAEUS -- a giant of Lybia, son of Poseidon and Gaea (Earth), invincible in wrestling because every time he was thrown to the earth (his mother), his strength was renewed. Hercules finally overcame him by holding him off the ground. *Cocytius anteus* (Ins).

ANTARES -- a constellation (Por), (Moll). Star-shaped.

ANTEDON -- a flowery nymph (Echin). Flowery.

ANTIGONE -- daughter of Oedipus (q.v.) put to death for burying her brother against the orders of Creon. Cf. Sophocles' *Antigone*. (Av). *Antigonia* and *Proantigonia* (Pisc).

ANTINOUS -- one of Penelope's suitors (Ann).

APOLLO -- (Phoebus) -- son of Zeus and Leto (Latonia), born on the island of Delos, musician, archer, healer, and god of Light and Truth. His oracle was at Delphi ("Delphian"). *Apollophanes* (Arach).

APHRODITE -- Goddess of Love and Beauty. According to Homer she was the daughter of Zeus and Dione (q.v.), hence "Dionea," but is more commonly said to have sprung from the foam (aphros) of the sea near Cythera, hence "Cytherea," (q.v.) whence she was wafted to the island of Cyprus, and so called "Cyprina" (q.v.). (Ann), *Aphroditidae* (Ann. marine worms noted for beauty); *Aphrodisiac*, a substance stimulating sexual desire; *Hermaphrodite* (Cf. Hermes).

ARACHNE -- peasant girl changed by Minerva into a spider because she had challenged the latter's skill in weaving. (Arach), *Arachnida*, because of spinning ability. *Arachniophyllum* (Coel. web-like structure), *Arachnactis* (Coel), *Arachnoides* (Echin), *Echinarachnius* (Echin). *Pyxis arachnoides* (Pisc. web-shaped scales). *Arachnidiam* (Ann).

ARBACES -- first king of Media. *Arbacia* (Echin).

ARCHEMORUS -- son of Lycurgus, killed by an adder. *Archemora* (Pl. adder shape).

ARCHIMEDES -- Greek mathematician (300 B.C.) who invented a water pump consisting of a spiral screw, called *Archimedes Screw*. (Bry. Screw-like axis).

ARCTURUS -- Boötes or "The Wagoner" who drives the "Wagon" or "Dipper." (Crust), *Arcturidae* (Crust).

ARETHUSA -- Greek maiden who was pursued by Alphaeus. She called on Artemis for help and was changed by her into a spring which flowed from Greece to Sicily. (Pl) (Amph), Arethusina (Moll). Spring-dwelling.

ARGES -- a Cyclops (q.v.). (Arach) (Pisc), *Arginae* (Pisc. falsely believed to inhabit the waters of live volcanoes), also, possibly, *Argas* and *Argasidae* (Arach) and *Argulus* and *Argulidae* (Crust), though these may come from ARGUS (q.v.).

ARGIOPE -- a nymph (Arach). (Moll) and *Argiopidae* (Moll).

ARGO -- ship on which Jason sailed to seek the Golden Fleece. (Moll) from resemblance of shell to ship and of tentacles to oars.

ARGONAUT -- sailor on the Argo. *Argonauta* (Moll), *Argonautites* (Moll).

ARGUS -- a mythical being with a hundred eyes whom Hera set to watch Io (q.v.). Hermes killed him but Hera placed his eyes in the tail of the peacock, whence (Av) and *Argusianus* (Av) from eyelike markings on feathers.

ARIADNE -- also spelled *Ariadna*, daughter of Minos (q.v.) who gave Theseus a ball of thread to guide him out of the Labyrinth (q.v.). (Arach). Nests of remarkable engineering skill. (Arach).

ARIEL -- a spirit of the air or water. (Av). Common name of African gazelle.

ARION -- 1) Greek poet who won a prize in a contest in Sicily. On his way home the sailors threatened to kill him. As a last request he asked to play on his lyre. He played so beautifully that the Dolphins were attracted. He jumped overboard and was borne by them to land. (Moll. from resemblance to lyre). *Arionellus* (Tril). *Ariolimax* (lyre-shaped shell), *Myarion*, *Arionta*, and *Ariophanta* (Moll). 2) First horse, offspring of Poseidon.

ARISTAEUS -- son of Apollo and Cyrene. He was a beekeeper and when
his bees were dying from some unknown cause, he asked his mother
what to do. She told him to consult Proteus (q.v.). He did so
but in order to get the information from Proteus he had to
overcome him. (Crust).

ARISTOTLE -- Greek philosopher and "Father of Biology" (384-322 B.C.).
Aristotle's Lantern -- Skeletal mouth structures of Echinoidea,
consisting of five converging processes, called "teeth," and many
hard ossicles. *Aristotelia racemosa* (Pl).

ARSINOE -- Egyptian queen (Ins), *Arsinoitherium* (Mam).

ARTEMIS -- Phoebus Apollo's twin sister, hence "Phoebe," a huntress and
goddess of the Moon (Selene). Also called Cynthia and Diana.
Artemia and *Artemidora* (Crust), *Artemesia* and *Artemesiaefolia*
(Pl), *Artemesina* (Por). *Perimyscus maniculatus artemesia* (Mam).

ASCLEPIOS -- god of Medicine, son of Apollo and Coronis. The latter
having been unfaithful was put to death, but her child was saved
and given to Chiron, the Centaur (q.v.), to bring up. The latter
taught Asclepios the art of healing in which he became so proficient
that he was even able to restore life. For this he incurred the wrath of
Zeus who struck him with a thunderbolt and killed him. His father
Apollo became so enraged at this that he killed many of Zeus' Cyclopes
(q.v.). But even after death he still healed folk who worshipped him
in his temples. Cf. Aesculapius. *Asclepias* (Pl), *Asclepiadaceae* (Pl),
Asclepiodora (Pl). Medicinal plants.

ASOPUS -- river god, father of Aegina (q.v.) who was carried off by Zeus.
Asopus asked the help of Sisyphus (q.v.).   (Ins), *Asopella*
(Arach).

ASPHODELUS -- "Meadow of the Dead" in Elysium, covered with either
Narcissus poeticus or *Asphodeline lutea*.   (Pl. daffodil), *Asphodeline*,
and *Puccinia asphodeli* (Pl).

ASTARTE -- Phoenician goddess of love, equivalent of Venus.   (Moll),
Astartidae (Moll), *Astartopsis* (Moll), *Parastarte* (Moll).

ASTRAEA -- goddess of justice and love, daughter of Zeus and Themis (Divine
Justice).   During the Golden Age she lived on earth but at the
end of it she was placed among the stars as the constellation
Virgo.   (Coel. star shaped).   *Astreidae* (Coel), *Astracopora* (Coel),
Goniastrea (Coel).

ATHENE -- daughter of Zeus and bearer of his shield. She sprang fully
armored from his head. She was the goddess of Wisdom and Purity,
hence "Parthenos," the virgin. Athens was her city; the olive, her
tree; and the owl, her bird, a symbol of wisdom. She was also called
Pallas Minerva. (Av).

ATLAS (antos) -- one of the Titans who, because he fought against Zeus, was condemned forever to bear the earth upon his shoulders. The first cervical vertebra which supports the skull. *Atlanta* (Moll), *Atlantosaurus* (Rept) derived indirectly through Atlantic Ocean habitat. *Attacus atlas* (Ins).

ATROPOS -- one of the Moirae (q.v.) or Fates so named because she "could not be turned" from her duty of cutting the thread of life. (Ins), *Atropa* (Pl). Source of belladonna and mandrake, narcotics. *Atropinae* (Pl) and atropine-alkaloid derived from *A. belladonna*. *Atropidae* -- book lice -- so called because it was thought they made a tapping noise on wood at the time of death, but the noise was probably due to the Death Watch Beetle (Thanks to Mr. E. D. Wilson, Mobile, Ala.)

ATTALUS -- king of Pergamus. *Attalea* (Pl).

AURELIAN -- Roman emperor. *Aurelianaster* (Echin), *Aureliania* (Coel).

AUVERUNCUS -- a god who warded off evil. (Pisc).

B

BASILISCUS -- fabulous serpent, lizard or dragon whose hissing would drive away all other serpents. From "basileus," king, hence "King of Serpents" and represented wearing a crown. According to the fable, it was born of a seven-year-old cock's egg during the days of the dog-star, Sirius, and hatched by a toad. Cf. Ley, *The Lungfish and the Unicorn*. (Rept) The Iguana has a membranous bag at the back of its head simulating crown of basilisk.

BEELZEBUTH OR BEELZEBUB -- (Heb. "Father of Flies"). A god of the Ekronites (II Kings, 1, 2) and to the Jews "the prince of demons" (Matt. XII, 24). *Cocytius beelzebuth* (Ins).

BELEROPHON -- son of Glaucas (Poseidon) who bridled the famous horse, Pegasus (q.v.) and rode him on many adventures, such as the destruction of the Chimaera (q.v.). He became too ambitious by trying to ride Pegasus to Olympus, was thrown off and wandered over the earth disconsolate (Moll).

BELISARIUS -- Byzantine general (505-565 A.D.). (Arach. fighter).

BELLONA -- goddess of war. (Av).

BEROE -- sister of Adonis and Aphrodite. (Cten), *Beroida*, *Beroidae*, and *Beroides* (Cten), and *Berosoma* (Coel).

BOLINA -- a nymph. (Cten), *Bolinopsis* (Coel). *Belinidae* (Cten), *Parabolina* and *Parabolinella* (Tril).

BOREAS -- the North Wind. He fell in love with Orithyia and when her father, Erechthaeus, opposed the suit, he swept down from the north and carried her away. Their sons Zetes and Calais went with Jason on the Quest of the Golden Fleece. *Boreaspis* (Pisc), *Boreonymphon* (Arthr), *Boroikon* (Mam), *Boriogale* (Mam), *Boreus* (Ins). Habitat. (Mam) and *Boreomysis* (Crust). *Nyctiborides* (Ins), *Bufo boreas* (Amph), *Cynoperca canadensis borea* (Pisc), *Boreofusus*, *Eutamias minimus borealis*, and *Odocoilus borealis* (Mam).

BRAHMA -- Hindu god. *Brahmatherium* (Mam).

BRIAREUS -- one of the Hecatonchires, hundred-handed monsters, sons of Uranus and Gaea. Other names: Aegyon, Cottus, Gyges, and Gyes. (Coel), *Briaraxis* (Ins), *Briaromys* (Mam). Having numerous tentacles. *Briareidae* (Coel). *Briareus*, virus of chicken pox, measles, and *herpes zoster*. Spreading quality. *Briareum* (Coel).

BRONTES -- one of the Cyclopes (q.v.) The "Thunderer." According to one myth, he was the father of Athene by Metis. *Brontornis* (Av), *Brontosaurus* (Rept), *Brontotherium* (Mam), *Brontozoum* (Rept). Huge size. (Ins), *Brontaeus* and *Bronteidae* (Tril), *Brontops* (Mam). (Ins).

BROTAEAS -- one of the Lapithae slain by the Centaur, Grynaeus, at the marriage of Perseus. (Crust). *Broteas* and *Broteochachtas* (Arach).

BYBLIS -- daughter of Miletus who loved her brother Caunus and followed him into many lands. She was changed into a fountain. (Pl) and *Byblidaceae* (Pl). Aquatic habitat.

C

CABEIRI -- magical dwarfs on the island of Lemnos who protected fruits. *Cabiropsidae* (Crust. parasitic on Isopoda).

CADUCEUS -- wand of Hermes (q.v.) with two oppositely twined serpents and surmounted by two wings. Symbol of medical profession.

CALENDAE -- the first day of the Roman month. *Calendula* (Pl) blooms monthly.

CALLIOPE -- ("beautiful-voiced") -- Chief of the Muses and Muse of Epic Poetry. (Av) beautiful voice.

CALLIRRHOE -- ("beautiful-flowing") -- 1) wife of Alcmaeon and cause of his death through her desire to obtain the necklace of Harmonia. 2) sea nymph, wife of Chrysaor. Beauty. (Pl).

CALLISTHENES -- friend of Alexander the Great. (Pl).

CALYPSO -- goddess of Silence who fell in love with Odysseus and held him prisoner. (Pl) same as *Cytheria* (q.v.).

CANDACES -- queen of Ethiopia. *Candace* and *Candacidae* (Crust).

CANOPUS -- pilot of Menelaus who was transformed into a star, Alpha Argus in the constellation of Argo. (Prot) star shape.

CASSIOPEIA -- queen of Ethiopia who set her beauty above that of the goddesses, for which her daughter, Andromeda (q.v.), was condemned to be devoured by a serpent. (Coel), *Cassiope* (Pl) and *Cassiopeium*, rare element. Star shape. *Cassiopea* (Coel).

CASTALIA -- fountain on Mt. Parnassus sacred to the Muses. (Moll) and (Pl), *Castaliella* (Moll). Aquatic habitat. (Ann).

CASTOR -- one of the *Dioscuri* (Cf. Pollux), twin sons of Zeus and Leda and brothers of Helen and Clytemnestra. When Castor was slain Pollux asked Zeus to let him die also. Zeus placed them in the heavens as the twin stars or *Gemini* (Astr). *Kosmoceras castor* (Mam), *Castoriidae* (Mam), *Castoroides* (Pal).

CECROPS -- founder and king of Athens. According to some, "born of a dragon, Dragon-shaped below." *Cecropia* (Pl) and (Ins). Larvae of latter (silk worm moth) feed on former (mulberry). *Cecrops* (Crust., parasite on tunny).

CENTAUR -- half man and half horse. Most famous was Chiron, the tutor of Asclepios. *Centauraea, Centaureum, Centauridium* (Pl) and *Centaury*, a tonic prepared from plant, said to have been discovered by Chiron (q.v.).

CEPHAEUS -- king of Ethiopia and father of Andromeda, changed into a star. star. *Cephaea* (Coel), *Cephaeus* (Arach). Star shape. *Cepheidae* (Coel).

CEPHALUS -- a hunter beloved by Eos (Dawn) who caused him accidentally to kill his wife, Procris. (Pisc). Great hunter.

CERBERUS -- three-headed, serpent-tailed and -girded watchdog of Erebus (q.v.), captured by Hercules in his twelfth "Labor." *Cerbera* (Pl). Shape. (Rept.)

CERCYON -- a robber killed by Theseus. (Ins). Robber instinct.

CERES -- goddess of corn, daughter of Cronus and Rhea. Also called Demeter. *Cereal* -- any edible grain. (Moll).

CEYX -- husband of *Alcyone* (q.v.) (Av), *Ceysia* (Ins), *Clytoceyx* (Av).

CHAOS -- shapeless nothingness (Cf. Introduction). (Prot) lack of definite shape.

CHARON -- son of Erebus (q.v.), ferryman of the Styx (q.v.). (Prot), *Charoniella* (Moll). *Charon evagatus*, virus of yellow fever -- deadly. *Charonaceae*.

CHARYBDIS -- whirlpool in the Straits of Messina opposite Scylla (q.v.). It figured in the adventures of the Argonauts, Odysseus, and Aenaeas. *Charybdea* (Coel), *Charybdella* (Coel), *Charybidae* (Coel), *Charybditeuthis* (Moll). Whirlpool-like shape. *Charybdia* (Pisc). *Charybdidae* (Coel).

CHEOPIS -- king of Egypt (2800-2700 B.C.). (Ins). Origin.

CHIMAERA -- monster formed of a lion in front, a serpent behind, and a goat in between. Killed by Bellerophon. *Chimaeridae* (Pisc), *Chimaira* (Pisc), *Chimaeropsylla* (Ins), *Chimarocephala* (Ins). Outlandish appearance. In genetics, a variegated flower, the result of diverse tissues growing together. *Chimaerichthys* and *Chimeropsis* (Pisc), *Chimarrogale* (Mam).

CHIONE -- a demigoddess. (Moll), *Ciona*, *Cione* and *Cionea* (Tun). *Chionea* (Ins).

CHIRON -- the chief of the Centaurs (q.v.). *Chironia* (Pl), *Hesperochiron* (Pl). *Hydrops chironius* (Rept).

CHRYSAOR -- a horse that sprang from the blood of the Medusa (q.v.). *Chrysaura* (Coel). Medusa form.

CIRCE -- a witch of Aenaea, daughter of Helios (q.v.), who turned men into beasts. Odysseus overcame her magic. (Moll), *Circaea* (Pl), *Circeaster* (Echin).

CLEODORA -- a Danaïd (Cf. Danaüs) (Moll). *Campaniclava cleodorae* (Coel. parasite on *Cleodora* (Moll).

CLEON -- an Athenian demagogue (d. 422 B.C.). *Cleonurus* (Ins), *Cleonolithus* (Ins), *Cleonus* (Ins).

CLETA -- one of the Graces. (Crust), *Cletopontius* (Crust). Graceful shape.

CLIO -- 1) Muse of History; 2) sister of Beroe. (Moll), *Cliodora* (Moll), *Clioites* (Por), *Cliona* (Por), *Clione* (Moll), *Clionolithes* (Por), *Archecliona* (Por). *Clionidae* (Por).

CLOTHO -- one of the three Fates, the Spinner of the Thread of Life. (Rept), *Clothelops* (Rept), *Clothonia* (Rept), *Amphiclotho* (Crust). *Clothilla* (Ins).

CLYMENE -- 1) a daughter of Ocean and mother of Atlas and Prometheus 2) mother of Phaëton (q.v.). (Mam), *Clymenia* (Moll). (Ann), *Clymenidae* (Ann).

CLYTEMNESTRA -- daughter of Tyndareus and Leda, wife of Agamemnon, and mother of Iphigenia. During Agamemnon's absence she fell in love with Aegisthus (q.v.) and, with him, murdered her husband and was herself killed by her son, Orestes. (Crust).

COCYTUS -- "river of lamentation" in the Underworld. Cf. Introduction. *Cocytia* (Ins).

COLIAS -- a name of *Aphrodite*. (Ins) Beauty.

CORNUCOPIA -- horn of plenty of Amalthaea (q.v.) *Cornucopiae* (Pl), *cornucopiate*, shaped like horn of plenty.

CORYBAS -- one of the Corybantes, priests of Cybele who worshipped her with mad frenzy. (Por.) *Corybantes* (Ins), *Corybissa* (Ins), *corybantism*, wild delirium with hallucinations. Habit.

COTTUS -- same as Briareus (q.v.). (Pisc) and *Cottidae* (Pisc). Numerous spines. *Cottunculus* (Pisc). *Cottogaster* (Pisc).

CROESUS -- a rich king. (Ins), *Croesomyrmex* (Ins).

CYBELE -- Phrygian goddess, equivalent of Rhea (q.v.), worshipped by the Corybantes (Cf. Corybas). (Arach). (Tril).

CYCHREUS -- son of Poseidon and Salamis. *Cychrocephalus* (Ins), *Cychrus* (Ins).

CYCLOPS -- one of the Cyclopes ("wheel-eyed"), gigantic monsters with a single eye in the middle of the forehead, offspring of Uranus (q.v.) and Gaea. They were banished for a time but later became the favorites of Zeus and forged his thunderbolts. The most famous of them was Polyphemus (q.v.). (Crust) and fetal monster, *Cyclopes* (Mam), *Cyclophis* (Rept), *Cyclopia* (Pl) and congenital defect in which the two orbits are fused into a single cavity containing one rudimentary eye. *Cyclopidae* (Crust), *Cyclopidius* (Mam), *Cyclopterus* and *Cyclopteridae* (Pisc. fins united to form sucking disc resembling median eye). *Cyclopterichthys* (Pisc). *Cyclopion* (Rept).

CYDIPPE -- priestess of Hera, mother of Biton and Cleobis, who yoked themselves to a car and drew her to Argos. (Arach), (Cten. two tentacles resembling a yoke), (Ins). *Cydippidae, Cydippidea* (Cten), *cydippiform stage* (Mertensia of *Lobata* and *Cestoidea*, having single pair of long tentacles resembling *Cydippe*).

CYGNUS -- name of three young men changed into swans and placed among the stars. (Av) and *Cygninae* (Av).

CYLLENE -- mountain where Hermes was born. (Ins).

CYMODOCE -- a nereid (q.v.). (Crust). *Cymodocea* (Pl). Marine habitat.

CYNTHIA -- name of Diana from Mt. Cynthus where she was born. (Tun), *Cynthiadae, Cynthiinae* and *Rhabdocynthia* (Tun), *Cynthiopsis* (Echin), *Halocynthia* (Tun). Bright coloration. *Philosamia cynthia* (Ins).

CYPRAEA -- name of Aphrodite (q.v.) from island of Cyprus. (Moll), *Cypraeidae* (Moll), from porcelain-like shell. *Cypraeovula* (Crust).

CYPRIS -- another form of above. (Crust. and larva of Cirripeds resembling), *Cypridae* (Crust), *Cypridina* and *Cypridinidae* (Crust), *cypridopathy* (venereal disease), *cypridophobia* or *cypriphobia* (fear of contracting venereal disease), *Cyprina* (Crust), *Cyprinidae* (Moll), *Cypripedium* (Pl. and Crust), *cypripedin* (tincture of root of Cypripedium used as an antispasmodic), *cyprinin* (protamine from the sperm of the carp), *Cyprinodont, Cyprinoidea, Cyprinoidae* and *Cyprinus* (Pisc. from great fertility). *Cyprinidae, Cyprininae, Cypriniformes, Cyprinion, Cyprinodon, Cyprinodontidae, Gymnocypris, Xenocypris* (Pisc). *Cypridopsis* (Crust), *Cyprinella* (Pisc), *Automeris cypria* (Ins).

CYRENE -- a water nymph, mother of Aristaeus by Apollo.   (Moll), *Cyrenodonta* (Moll), *Cyrenodonax* (Moll).   Habitat.   *Cyrenella, Cyrenellidae, Cyrenidae* (Moll).

CYTHEREA -- another name of Aphrodite from island of Cythera near which she arose from sea.   (Moll) (Pl), *Cythere* (Crust), *Cytherella* and *Cytherellidae* (Crust), *Cytheridae* (Crust).   Beauty.   *Cytheromania* (nymphomania).

D

DAEDALUS -- ("cunning worker") architect who built the Labyrinth (q.v.) of Crete for King Minos. He helped Theseus to escape from it and for this was imprisoned along with his son, Icarus, in it. He made wings for the two of them and they escaped.   (Ins), *Daedalea* (Pl. because of labyrinthiform lamellae formed by pores), *Daedalopelta* (Por), *Daidalometra* (Echin), *daedaloid* (Labyrinthform), *Daedalochia* (Moll), *daedalean* -- pertaining to.

DANAUS -- mythical king of Arabia and father of the Danaids. There were fifty of them. They were forced into marriage and on the night of the marriage all but one, Hypermnestra, killed their husbands. For this they were condemned in Hades to forever draw water in leaky vessels. (Ins) *Danai* (Pl), *Danaidae* and *Danainae* (Ins). *Danais* and *Danaides* (Ins).

DAPHNE -- ("shy") daughter of the river god, Peneus, and a huntress. She was uninterested in marriage and when Apollo fell in love with her and pursued her, she called on her father for help and he changed her into a laurel tree.   But Apollo still loved her and chose the laurel as his tree and with its leaves crowned the brows of victors. (Crust) (Pl. *D. mezereum*, the bay tree from which *mezereum* obtained), *Daphnia* == *Daphne* (Crust), *Daphnidae* (Crust), *Daphnidium* (Pl), *Daphnaeoderma* (Moll), *Daphniopsis* (Crust), *Chamaedaphne* (Pl), *daphnin* (glucoside from mezereum), *daphnitin* (dioxycumarin from daphnin). *Daphnella* (Moll and Crust).

DARDANUS -- son of Electra (q.v.) and founder of the Trojan race. *Dardania* (Moll).

DAULIAS -- epithet of Philomela (q.v.) from Daulis, city near which she was turned into a bird. (Av).

DELPHI -- shrine of Apollo under Mt. Parnassus. *Delphinidae* (Mam), *Delphinium* (Pl has dolphin-shaped nectary), *delphinine*, *delphocurarine* and *delphinoidine* (drugs derived from *Delphinium*), *Delphinus*, *Delphinapterus* (Mam) and *Delphinoidea* (Mam). The *Dolphin* was sacred to Apollo. *Delphis* and *Prodelphinus* (Mam). *Delphinapterus* and *Priscodelphinus* (Mam).

DERCETIS -- Syrian goddess, half woman, half fish. (Pisc) (Ins), *Dercetum* (Myr). *Dercetidae* (Pisc). Fish shape.

DEVERRA -- goddess of the broom. (Pl).

DIANA -- Roman goddess identified with Artemis (q.v.) (Ins), (Pisc), (Mam), *Dianella* (Pl) (Moll).

DIDO -- Queen of Carthage who entertained Aeneas. *Metamorpha dido* (Ins).

DIEDEMIA -- daughter of Lycomedes, king of Scyros. (Pl).

DIOGENES -- Greek philosopher (412-323 B.C.) who lived for a long time in a tub. (Crust. from eremitic habit).

DIOMEDES -- son of Tydaeus and a famous warrior in the Trojan War. The mourners at his funeral were turned into birds. *Diomedea* (Av). *Diomedeinae* (Av).

DIONE -- the mother of Aphrodite according to one version, who, therefore, was called "Dionaea." (Ins), *Dionaea* (Pl).

DIOSCORIDES -- Greek physician and botanist. *Dioscorea* and *Dioscoraceae* (Pl), *dioscorein* (resin from), *dioscorine* (alkaloid from), *Dioscorides' Granule* (lactose, gum arabic and arsenous acid).

DIOS -- genitive of Zeus. *Diospyros* (Pl), "Jupiter's Wheat" extract of *D. virginiana*, astringent. *Dianthus* (Pl).

DIRCE -- wife of Lycus, who because of the cruel treatment of Antiope was put to death and thrown into a spring near Thebes, since called by her name. *Dirca* (Pl), *Dircaea* (Ins).

DORIS -- daughter of Ocean (q.v.), wife of Nereus and mother of the Nereids (q.v.). (Moll), *Dorididae* (Moll), *Doridella* (Moll), *Doridopsis* (Moll), *Doridunculus* (Moll), *Dorippe, Dorippidae* (Crust). Habitat. *Doridium* (Moll).

DOTO -- a Nereid. (Moll), *Dotonidae* (Moll). Same.

DRYAS -- one of the Dryads, nymphs of the trees (from "drys" -- oak tree). (Pl). *Dryalestes* (Mam), *Dryomyzidae* (Ins), *Dryopithecus* (Mam), *Dryopthorus* (Ins). *Drymarchon, Drymobius, Dryodophis, Ophiodrys, Philodryas* (Rept). Tree snakes.

DRYOPE -- daughter of Dryops and sister of Iole. For plucking a flower from a tree which was in reality the nymph *Lotis*, she was turned into a tree. (Crust, tree-like).

E

ECHIDNA -- ("viper") a monster, half woman and half serpent, mother by Typhon (q.v.) of the Sphinx, Chimaera and other monsters. (Mam. monstrous appearance). *Echidnocephalus* (Pisc). *Proechidna* (Mam).

EIRENE -- goddess of peace. *Eirenis* (Rept), *Irena* (Av), *Irenesauripus* (Rept), *Irenomys* (Mam). Peacefulness.

ELECTRA -- daughter of Agamemnon, whose love for her murdered father led her to connive in the death of her mother. Cf. Euripedes' and Sophocles' *Electra*. (Pl. same as *Laodice* q.v.), (Coel), (Moll), (Mam). Also *Electra Complex*, father complex, opposite to *Oedipus Complex* (q.v.).

ELEUSINE -- a name for Ceres (p.v.) from Eleusis, the town where she was worshipped with the Eleusinian Mysteries. (Pl), *Eleusina* (Ins).

ELYSIUM -- place of blessedness on the islands of the Western Ocean. *Elysia* and *Elysiidae* (Moll) from wing-like expansions of body. *Ilysia* and *Ilysiidae* (Rept).

EMPOUSA -- a hobgoblin associated with Hecate (q.v.) having a vampire's appetite for flesh. (Pl) parasitic habit. *Empusa* (Ins).

ENDYMION -- a shepherd with whom Selene (q.v.) fell in love and put to sleep forever. (Pl) (Tril).

ENYO -- goddess of war (Arach == *Zodarion*) and *Enyoidae* (Arach). (Ins).

EOLIDES -- a descendant of Aeolus (q.v.), king of the winds. *Eolida* (Moll).

EOS -- goddess of Dawn. (Av) (Pisc). *Eoanthropus* and *Eohippus* (Mam), *Eoscorpius* (Arach). Primitive.

ERATO -- the muse of love poetry. (Moll), (Ins), Eratia (Ins), Eratotrivia (Moll).

EREBUS -- the Underworld as a whole or only the upper portion of it. Cf. Introduction. (Ins), *Erebia* (Ins), *Erebophis* (Rept), *Erebothrix* (Ins). Habitat.

ERINYS -- the three Furies or Eumenides: Alecto, Megaera, and Tisiphone, inhabitants of the Underworld who sprang from the blood of Uranus. They had snakes for hair and wept blood. At first they were supposed to punish evildoers but later were regarded as benignant. They were worshipped at Colonus. *Erynnis* (Tril) and (Ins). Behavior.

EROS -- in early stories he was the offspring of Nyx and Erebus (cf. Introduction) and was regarded as "the moving force within and about all things" (Fox). Later he was referred to as Aphrodite's son and his role changed to that of a matchmaker. (Ins), *Erotolepsia* (Ins), *erotic*, *eroticism* (pertaining to sex).

ERYCINA -- a name of Venus from her temple in Erycus, Sicily. (Ins), *Erycinidae*, *Erycinides* (Ins). Beauty. (Moll), *Erycinidae* (Moll).

ERYTHEIA -- an island in the Hesperides (q.v.) where Geryon (q.v.) dwelt, from from the trees with golden (erythos) apples. *Erythea* (Pl) from color of fruit.

ERYTHRAE -- a town in Asia Minor where the sibyl, Herophile, thought to be the same as the Cumaean Sibyl (q.v.) dwelt. *Erythraeidae* (Ins). Probably habitat.

ERYX -- king of Sicily, opponent of Hercules. (Rept). *Erycides* (Ins).

EUNICE -- a Neried. (Ann), *Eunicea* (Coel), *Euniceopsis* (Coel), *Eunicicola* (Arthrop), *Eunicidae* (Ann). Marine habitat. *Eunicella* (Coel), *Eunicites* (Ann).

EUPHRONIDES -- son of Nyx (Cf. Introduction). (Echin).

EUPHROSYNE -- Grace of Mirth and Joy. (Ann).

EUROS -- the East or Southeast Wind. (Ins).

EUTERPE -- Muse of lyric poetry. (Pl).

EURYALE -- one of the Gorgons (q.v.) (Pl) and (Echin), *Euryalidae* (Echin), *Euryalonia* (Rept). Resemblance to snaky hair. *Euryalus* (Ins).

F

FAUNA -- the animal life of a region from Fauna, Roman goddess of the fields. Also known as Maia (q.v.) and Bona Dea. She was the wife of Vulcan.

G

GALANTHIS -- an attendant of Alcemone, changed into a weasel. *Galanthia* (Ins), *Galanthis* (Crust), *Galanthula* (Coel). Shape.

GALATEA -- 1) sea nymph, sister of Doris (q.v.), and beloved by Polyphemus (q.v.); 2) a statue carved by Pygmalion, which Venus brought to life. (Moll), same as *Galathea* (Crust), *Galateidae* or *Galatheidae* (Crust), *Galatheascus* (Crust), *Galathodes* (Crust). Habitat. *Hyale galateae* (Crust).

GANYMEDE -- a son of Laomedon, carried to Olympus by eagle of Zeus and made cupbearer of the gods. *Ganymeda* (Echin), *Ganymedebdella* (Echin). Cup shape.

GERYON OR GERYONE -- a three-bodied monster, son of Chrysoar and Callirrhoe (q.v.), who kept cattle on the island of Erytheia (q.v.). The tenth "Labor" of Hercules was to bring back these cattle. (Coel) under both forms of name, *Geryonia* (Coel), *Geryonidae* (Coel). Shape. (Crust).

GLAUCUS -- the word means "white" or "shining" and has been used of animals for this reason. However, there were several noted characters who had the epithet for a proper name for some similar reason, among them the helmsman of the Argo (q.v.) who became a divinity of the sea, and a Lycian prince who foolishly exchanged his shining golden armor for the dull brazen armor of Diomedes (q.v.). (Moll), (Ins) and (Pisc), Glaucidium (Av), Glaucoma (Prot G. scintillans has, moreover, a membrane of the mouth oening whose motion resembles the winking of an eye), *Glaucopis* (Av. == *Callaeas*), *Glaucomys* and *Glauconycteris* (Mam), *Glaucosoma* (Pisc), *Glauconia* (Rept), *Glauconome* (Coel), *Glaucomya* (Moll). Glaucoma, a disease of the eye.

GOLIATH -- giant slain by David. (Amph) (Av), Goliathiceras (Moll), Goliathicera (Ins), Goliathus (Ins). Large size.

GORDIUS -- king of Phrygia, father of Midas (q.v.). He came into a town and tied his team in the temple. It was said that anyone who could untie the knot would become lord of Asia. This was the famous Gordian Knot which Alexander the Great cut with his sword. (Nemat), *Gordiaceae* and *Gordiidae* (Nemat. rope-like), *Gordiichthys* (Pisc), *Gordiodrilus* (Ann), *Polygordius* (Ann. habit of twisting into a knot).

GORGON -- one of three mythical creatures who had snakes for hair. Cf. Medusa. (Coel), *Gorgonia*, *Gorgonella*, *Gorgoniidae*, *Gorgonina*, *Gorgonacea*, *-gorgia* (comb. form of genera, e.g., *Eugorgia*), *-gorgiidae* (comb. form of families, e.g., *Chrysogorgiidae*) (Coel), *Gorgonocephalus* (Echin), *Gorgonopsia* (Rept), *Gorgosaurus* (Rept), *gorgonin* (albumenoid derived from *Gorgonia*). Snakelike appendages. *Epistor gorgon* (Ins), *Gorgodera* (Platy).

GRYPHUS -- a Griffin, Gryphon or Griffon, one of the "hounds of Zeus." They had the body of a lion, the head and wings of an eagle. They guarded the gold of the North. (Av), *Pseudogryphus* (Av), *Gryphaea* (Moll), *Gryphochiton* (Moll), *Grypotherium* (Mam), *Griffon* (breed of dog). Eagle-like beak or snout.

GYGES -- same as *Briareus* (q.v.). Gygis (Av).

H

HAEMON -- son of Creon to whom Antigone was betrothed. *Harmonia*.

HALCYON -- same as *Alcyone* (q.v.). (Av), *Halcyoninae* (Av), *Halcyornis* (Av).

HAMADRYAS -- a wood nymph whose life began and ended with a particular tree. (Ins), (Mam), *Hamadryopsis* (Ins), *hamadryad* (Rept). Forest habitat.

HANNIBAL -- Carthaginian general (247-183 B.C.) in Second Punic War. *Protoparce hannibal* (Ins).

HARPY -- creatures with hooked (Gr. harpe -- hook) beaks, spiked tails and a terrible stench. Also called the "hounds of Zeus." The Argonauts and Aeneas had encounters with them. *Harpy Eagle* (*Pithecophaga jefferyi*), *Harpyia* or *Harpyja*, *Harpyhaliaetus*, *Harpyopsis* (Av with hooked beaks), *Harpyia* and *Harpionycteris* (Mam with eagle-like snout). Allied (from *harpe*) are *Harpa*, *Harpagornis* and *Harpagus* (Av) and *Harpiocephalus harpia* (Mam).

HEBE -- goddess of Youth, daughter of Zeus and Hera, and wife of Hercules after his deification. She was cupbearer to the gods before Ganymede. *Hebecephalus* (Ins), *Hebelona* (Pl), *hebetic* (pertaining to youth), *hebin* (gonadotropic extract of the anterior pituitary). As a common noun it signifies "youth," "adolescence" and is synonymous with Latin *pubis*. It is used as a combining form meaning to have the structure or condition at an early stage of life, e.g., *hebeanthous*, *hebecarpous*, *hebecladous*, *hebegynous*, *hebepetalous*, *hebephrenia*. It is also used in reference to the *as pubis*, e.g., *hebeosteotomy* or *hebotomy* (breaking of the pubic symphysis to facilitate parturition). *Hebella* and *Hebellidae* (Coel).

HECATE -- a name of Artemis (q.v.) as goddess of the Lower World, of the Dark of the Moon, and of the Crossways. In this last role she is represented as having three heads and six arms and carrying a torch and a spear. (Nem), *Hecatesia* (Ins).

HECTOR -- son of Priam and famous warrior of Troy. (Ins).

HELICON -- mountain where the Muses dwelt. *Heliconius*, Heliconiidae, and *Heliconiides* (Ins). Beauty.

HELIOS -- the sun god, son of Hyperion (q.v.). Many biological names are derived from it. The reference is either directly to the sun or to some structure with a sun-like appearance. *Helarctes* (Mam), *-helia* (combining form of genera of Coel., e.g., *Amphihelia*), *Helianthemum* (Pl), *Heliaster*, *Heliasteridae* (Echin), *Helicrysum* (Pl), *Heliochaera* (Ins) (Av. from tuft on head), *Heliodrilus* (Ann), *Heliolites*, *Proheliolites*, *Heliolitidae* (Coel), *Heliornis* (Av), *Heliopais* (Av. tropical habitat), *Heliopora*, *Helioporidae* (Coel), *heliophobia* (fear of the sun), *heliosis* (sun stroke), *Helioster* (Av. beauty), *heliotaxis* (attraction toward the sun), *Heliothis* (Ins), *Heliothrix* (Av), *heliotropin* (essence of *Heliotropium*), *heliotropism* (a turning toward the sun), *Heliozoa* (Prot), *Heliphobius* (Mam. subterranean habitat), *Helochares* (Ins). Also *Eliocidaris* (Echin), *Ichthelis* (Pisc). *Helicops* (Rept). Color.

HEPHAESTUS (VULCAN) -- son of Zeus and Hera, god of fire, armorer (Mulciber) of the gods and patron of blacksmiths. *Hephaestic* or *Hephestic* (relating to blacksmiths, e.g., *hephaestic hemiplegia*, a neurosis marked by paresis of the forearm).

HERCULES OR HERAKLES -- son of Zeus and Alcmene, celebrated for strength, especially for achieving "Twelve Labors." *Dynestes hercules* Hercules Beetle (Ins), largest existing insect. *Hercules Allheal* (Pl. *Opopanax chironium*), *Hercules Club* (Pl. *Zanthoxylum clava-herculis*).

HERO -- priestess of Aphrodite beloved by Leander who used to swim the Hellespont to visit her. (Moll).

HERCYNA -- attendant of Persephone. (Ins), *Hercynella* (Ins), *Hercynosaurus* (Rept). Subterranean habitat.

HERMAPHRODITUS -- son of Hermes and Aphrodite. While bathing in a pool sacred to the nymph. Salmacis, he became united in one body with her. (Mam), *hermaphrodite* (having both sexes in the same individual).

HERMES -- son of Zeus and Maia. He was the messenger of Zeus and is represented with wings on his feet and on the flat hat he wore. He carried a wand of coiled snakes, the Caduceus (q.v.). The Romans called him Mercury. *Hermaea, Hermaeidae* (Moll), *Hermatobates* (Ins), *Hermeophaga* (Arthrop), *Hermetia* (Ins), *hermidin* (chromogen substance extracted from *Mercurialis pernennis*), *Herminea* (Arthrop), *Herminidae* (Arthrop), *Hermippus* (Arach), *Hermodactylus* (Pl). He was also the "revealer of esoteric doctrines," whence *hermetic art* (alchemy), *hermetic medicine* (iatro-medicine or Paracelsian), *hermetically sealed* (air tight).

HERMIONE -- daughter of Helen and Menelaus. (Ann), Herminionina (Ann).

HEROPHILUS -- Alexandrian physician (335-280 B.C.). *Torcular Herophili* (Herophilus' Wine-Press or Confluence of Sinuses).

HESIONE -- 1) daughter of Laomedon, king of Troy, rescued from a sea monster by Hercules; 2) wife of Prometheus, a sea nymph. *Hesionidae* (Ann). Marine habitat.

HESPER OR HESPERUS -- the evening star. See also VESPER.

HESPERA -- one of the Hesperides.

HESPERIA -- the lands of the west; to the Greeks, Italy and Spain.

HESPERIDES -- the daughters of Atlas (hence also Atlantides): Aegle, Hespera (Hestia), and Erytheis (Erytheia) who guarded the trees with golden apples (probably oranges) which Hercules obtrained in his eleventh "Labor." Also used of the garden. Many biological terms are derived from these names. The significance is usually western habitat or something to do with the evening or, finally, a reference to the "golden apples." *Hesperanopia* (night blindness), *Hesperia, Hesperiidae* (Ins), *hesperidene* (dextro - limonene), *hesperidin* (glucoside), *hesperidium* (a syncarpous, polycarpellous, many-celled fruit, e.g., the orange), *Hesperiphona* (Av), *Hesperis* (Pl), (Rept), *hesperitin* (a sugar), *Hesperocallis* (Pl), *Hesperochiron* (Pl), *Hesperodrilus* (Ann), *Hesperoleucus* (Pisc), *Hesperornis* (Av), *Hesperopitheci* (Mam), *hesperus* (Pipestrellus and Thomomys -- Mam).

HESTIA -- (Vesta) sister of Zeus, goddess of the hearth. In Rome, her fire was tended by six Vestal Virgins. (Ins).

HIPPOCAMPUS -- a sea horse on which the gods rode. (Pisc), *Hippocampidae* (Pisc). A part of the brain shaped like the sea horse.

HIPPOCRATES -- Greek physician and "Father of Medicine" (460-377 B.C.). *Hipporatea* or *Hypocratea, Hippocrataceae* (Pl). *Hippocratic Oath*, an ethical pledge attributed to Hippocrates. Erratum: *"Hipporatea"* for *"Hippocratea."*

HIPPODAMIA -- 1) wife of Pirithoüs, friend of Hercules; 2) wife of Pelops. (Ins). *Machaerosema hippodamia* (Ins).

HIPPOLYTE -- queen of the Amazons and mother of Hippolytus. She was killed by Hercules during his ninth "Labor" which was to bring back her girdle. (Crust).

HIPPOLYTUS -- son of Theseus and Hippolyte. He was unjustly accused of killing Theseus' wife, Phaedra, and was banished by his father. On the way, he was dragged to death by his horses. Some say it was he who was brought back to life by Asclepios (q.v.). (Crust) and *Hippolytidae* (Crust).

HIPPOMEDON -- one of the "Seven Against Thebes" who fought with Polyneices against his brother, Eteocles. They were the sons of Oedipus. (Crust).

HORAE -- goddesses of the seasons: Dike (Justice), Eirene (Peace), and Eunomia (Wise Legislation). *Horaeocera* (Ins). *Horaeometra* (Echin).

HYACINTHUS -- friend of Apollo. One day when they were competing in throwing the discus, Apollo struck him with it and killed him. From his blood sprang a beautiful red flower which, according to Thistleton-Dyer and Hart,* was *Scilla bifolia* but later the cult of Hyacynthus was transferred to the blue larkspur, *Hyacinthus sparte*, now *Delphinium ajacis.*   (Pl), *Hyacinthia* (Coel), *Neurotrichus hyacinthinus* (Mam), *Phytomonas hyacinthis* (Pl parasite of hyacinth), *Scilla hyacinthoides* (Pl).

HYAS -- one of the daughters (Hyades) of Atlas. They were half sisters of the Pleides. They were set among the stars by Zeus for taking care of Dionysius (q.v.) when he was a baby. (Amph).

HYDRA -- a monster with nine serpent heads whom Hercules was ordered to kill in his second "Labor." The difficulty of this was that when one head was cut off, two grew back in its place. But Hercules solved this problem with the aid of his nephew, Iolaus, who seared off the necks as Hercules cut the heads off. The last head was immortal but Hercules disposed of it by burying it under a rock. The term is applied to many animals with tentacles and also to serpents.   (Coel), *Hydractinea, Hydrallamania* (Coel), *hydranth* (a polyp of a colonial coelenterate), *Hydraria* (Coel), *Hydraspis* (Rept), *Hydraspotherium* (Mam), *Hydridae* (Coel), *hydriform* (having form of Hydra), *Hydrichthys* (Coel parasitic on fish), *hydrocaulus* (stem of colonial coelenterate), *Hydrocorallia* and *Hydrocorallina* (Coel), *hydroid*

---

* *A Companion to Greek Studies;* Ed. L. Whitley, Cambridge, 1931.

(similar to Hydra), *Hydroidae* and *Hydroidea* (Coel), *Hydroides* (Ann), *Hydromedusa* (Coel and Rept), *hydrorhiza* (network of materials to which hydroids attach), *Hydrurus* (Prot).

HYGEA OR HYGEIA -- goddess of Health, said by some to have been a daughter of Aesculapius (q.v.) and, by others, his wife.

HYMEN -- god of the Wedding Feast. Used to indicate a membrane from the membrane closing the vagina. The term is applied to many forms with membranous structures. (Pl), *Hymenacea* (Pl), *Hymenancora* (Por), *Hymenaster* (Echin), *Hymeniacidon* (Por), *Hymenitis* (Ins), *hymenium* (portion of hypha in fungi forming spore mother-cells), *Hymenocallis* (Pl), *Hymenocaris* (Crust), *Hymenocephalus* (Pisc), *Hymenochirus* (Amph), *Hymenoclea* (Pl), *Hymenodes* (Ins), *Hymenodon* and *Hymenodora* (Crust), *Hymenolaemus* (Av), *Hymenolepis* (Platy), *Hymenophyllum* (Pl), *Hymenoptera* (Ins), *Hymenopus* (Ins), *Hymenosoma* and *Hymenosomatidae* (Crust). *Hymenostomum* (Pl).

HYPERBOREANS -- a strange people who lived beyond the North Wind across Ocean. *Hyperborea* (Ins) (Moll found on the coast of Spitzbergen). Habitat.

HYPERION -- a Titan, father of the Sun, Moon and Dawn, later identified with Apollo, god of manly beauty. (Ins), *Hyperia* (Crust), *Hyperiodrilus* (Ann). Beauty. *Hyperioides, Hyperiidea, Hyperiidae, Hyperiopsis,* and *Hyperiopsidae* (Crust).

HYPNUS -- god of sleep, father of Morpheus, Icelus and Phantasus, and twin brother of Thanatos (Death). *Hypnea* (Pl), *Hypnorna* (Ins) *Hypnos* (Pisc-electric ray), *hypnosis* (an induced condition resembling sleep), *hypnospore* (a resting spore), *Hypnota* (Ins), *Hypnoticus* (Crust), *hypnotoxin* (hypothetical substance producing sleep), *Phylypnus* (Pisc). From either habit of hibernation or of paralysing prey.

I

IAPYX -- said by some to be the son of Daedalus. The Iapyges were inhabitants of southeastern Italy. (Ins) also spelled *Japyx, Iapygidae* or *Japygidae* (Ins), *Heteroiapyx* (Ins).

ICARUS -- son of Daedalus (q.v.). When escaping from the Labyrinth he flew too near the sun and his wings melted and he fell into the sea near the island of Icaria. *Icaria* (Ins), *Icariastrum* (Ins), *Icaridon* (Ins). Power of flight. *Icaroscope* -- a telescope which views afterglow image of sun on transparent phosphor screen.

ICELUS -- son of Hypnus. He gives dreams of birds and beasts. (Arach), (Pisc), *Icelichthys* (Pisc), *Icelinus* (Pisc).

IDMON -- father of Arachne. *Idmonea* (Bry) (Ann), *Idmonia* (Arach).

IDOMONEUS -- king of Crete and leader of the Cretans in the Trojan War. (Mam).

IDOTHEA OR EIDOTHEA -- a sea nymph. (Crust) also *Idotea*. Marine.

INACHUS -- son of Ocean, king of Argos and a river god. (Crust), *Inachidae* and *Inachoides* (Crust) and father of Io. Aquatic.

INCUBUS -- a demon who caused nightmares. (Ins).

INDRA -- Hindu god of thunderstorms. *Indrabovis, Indratherium* (Mam). Indian habitat.

INO -- daughter of Cadmus, wife of Athamas and stepmother of Phrixus. She hated the latter and to get rid of him she parched all the seed corn so that there was a famine in the land. Then she paid an oracle to tell Athamas that the only way to overcome this was to offer his son Phrixus in sacrifice. As he was about to do this a ram with golden fleece snatched him and his sister, Helle, up and flew with them over the straits between Europe and Asia. Helle fell into the water, since called the Hellespont, but Phrixus went on to Colchis. Later Athamas killed Ino's son, Melicertes (q.v.), and she took his body into her arms and jumped into the sea where she was turned into a sea goddess and later saved Odysseus from drowning. (Moll) and *Inoceramus* (Moll). Marine habitat.

IO -- daughter of Inachus. Zeus fell in love with her and when Hera was on the point of discovering her with him he changed Io into a heifer. But Hera suspecting the ruse, asked for the heifer and put her in charge of Argus (q.v.). She was released by Hermes. Then Hera sent a gadfly to torment her. She wandered over the earth, met and consoled Prometheus and finally reached the Nile where Zeus changed her back to human form and had a son, Epephus, by her from whom Hercules was descended. The Ionian Sea and the Bosphorus (Ford of the Cow) are named after her. (Ins), (Moll).

IOLE -- daughter of King Eurytus. She was taken captive by Hercules. His wife Deianira became jealous of her and gave Hercules a robe dipped in the blood of the Centaur Nessus which caused him terrible agony and finally led him to commit suicide. She also killed herself when she learned of the effect it produced on her husband. (Av) Beauty.

IPHIGENIA -- daughter of Agamemnon and Clytemnestra. When the Greek fleet assembled at Aulis to sail for Troy it was not able to proceed because of storms. A soothsayer told the chiefs that these were due to the anger of Artemis because some of the soldiers had killed a hare dear to her and that the only way to appease her was to sacrifice Agamemnon's daughter, Iphigenia. According to one account this was done and Agamemnon later paid for the foul deed with his own life. But a later tale is that Iphigenia was snatched from the pyre by Artemis and taken by her to Tauris (Crimea) and made a priestess in her temple. Years later Iphigenia was instrumental in saving the life of her

brother, Orestes, and, in turn, was rescued by him. She is the subject
of two plays by Euripides, *Iphigenia in Aulis*, and *Iphigenia in Taurus*. (Moll).

IPHIS -- one of the Argonauts (q.v.) (Ins), (Crust), *Iphisa* (Rept).

IRENA -- same as Eirene (q.v.) (Av. the fairy blue bird).

IRIS -- goddess of the Rainbow and messenger of the gods. Signifies beauty,
color, light. (Pl), (Ins), *Iradaceae* (Pl), *Trutta irideus* (Pisc), *Iridina* (Moll),
Iridodrilus (Ann), *Iridogorgia* (Coel), *Iridomyrmex* (Ins), *Irodormis* (Av). As a
common noun: 1) the colored part of the eye; 2) the inner circle of the
ocellus of the butterfly's wing;   3) an adjustable diaphragm to regulate
the amount of light in optical instruments. Also: *Iridaceous* (pertaining
to Irises), *Iridin* (glucoside from Iris), *Iridium* (white, iridescent metal),
Iridocyte (guanin crystals in skin cells of certain animals), *Iridophore*
(chromatophore formed of guanin crystals).

ISIS -- Egyptian goddess of fecundity. (Coel), *Isidae* (Coel), *Isidella* (Coel),
Isisina (Coel), *Isidium* (Pl -- lichen resembling coral and wartlike
outgrowth on certain lichens). Beauty.

IULUS -- a name of Ascanius, son of Aeneas. (Moll).

J

JACCHUS -- twentieth day of the celebration of the Eleusinian Mysteries,
so called from the cry raised by the people during the procession with
the statue of Bacchus. (Mam -- from habit of crying out).

JANUS -- Roman God represented with two faces. His temple on the
Janiculum Hill was closed during peace. January is named after
him.   His wife is called Jana.   (Moll), (Ins), *Janella*, *Janellidae*
(Moll), *Janulus* (Arach). *Janusia* (Moll). Also *Janus Brown* and *Green*
(biological dyes).

JUBA -- king of Numidia. *Jubaea* (Pl).

JUGURTHA -- king of Numidia. *Jugurthia* (Ins).

JULUS -- same as *Iulus*.   (Myr), *Julidae*, *Juloidea*, *Julopsis* (Myr).   Also
combining form, e.g., *Blanjulus* (Myr).

JUNO -- the Roman equivalent of Hera, wife of Zeus. Called "Ox-eyed" by
Vergil. *Automeris junonia* (Ins). Markings.

JYNX -- the Wryneck (Av) named from its cry. Witches used to bind it to a
wheel and turn around to drive out evil from soul.

L

LABDACUS -- father of Oedipus. (Arach == Senoclus).

LABYRINTH -- a maze constructed by Daedalus for Minos, king of Crete,
in which to keep the Minotaur, a monster half man and half
bull.   Hence any complex structure such as the *Bony* and *Mem-*

branous Labyrinth of the ear, the uriniferous tubules of the kidney. *Labyrinthibranchi* (Pisc), *Labyrinthici* (Pisc. complex structure of gills), *Labyrinthodon* (Amph. complex pattern of teeth), *Labyrinthula* (Prot. complex structure forming false plasmodium), *Labyrinthulidae* (Prot), *Labyrinthus* (Mol == Helix).

LACHESIS -- one of the three Moirae or Fates, the Disposer of Lots, who assigned to every man his destiny. Hence deadly. (Rept. the "Bush-master," most poisonous snake in Western Hemisphere), *Laches* (*Lachesis*), *Lachesana* (Arach), *Lachesilla* (Ins. abortive genus of Neuroptera proposed by Westwood to complete the trilogy of *Atropos*, *Clotho*, and *Lachesis*. Cf. *Cambridge Natural History*, V, 395 Note).

LADAS -- a runner of Alexander the Great, famous for speed. (Moll).

LAELIA -- a Vestal Virgin. (Pl), (Ins), *Laelicae* (Pl), *Laeliopsis* (Ins).

LAESTRYGONS -- cannibalistic giants who murdered the comrades of Odysseus. *Laestrigonus* (Crust), *Laestrigonus* (Arach). Cannibalism?

LAIS -- name of two Greek courtesans noted for beauty. (Arach), (Pisc).

LALAGE -- a girl in Horace's Odes. (Av).

LAMACHUS -- an Athenian. (Ins), *Lamechella* (Ins).

LAMIA -- a monster with the head and breast of a woman and the body of a serpent who fed on human flesh; hence a vampire. (Ins), *Lamiasaurus* (Rept), *Lamictis* (Mam), *Lamiidae* (Ins).

LAOCOON -- a priest of Apollo at Troy who was destroyed with his sons by serpents because he threw a spear at the Trojan Horse. *Citheronia laocoon* (Ins).

LAODICEA -- city in Phrygia named after Laodice, a nymph, or the same as Electra (q.v.). (Coel).

LAOMEDON -- king of Troy and father of Priam, slain by Hercules for refusing the reward promised him for saving Hesione (q.v.) *Laomedea* (Coel), *Laomedes* (Coel).

LARENTIA -- 1) nurse of Romulus and Remus and mistress of Hercules; 2) a name of Flora (q.v.). (Ins), *Larentiidae* (Ins), *Larentioides* (Ins).

LAR(ES) -- spirits of the ancestors. They were associated with the Penates, gods of the hearth and guardians of the storehouse. (Mam. from white feet, ghostlike), (*L.sabellorum* -- Coel. parasite on tubes of *Sabella*), *Laria* (Ins), *Lariidae* (Ins). (Mam) White hands and feet, hence ghost-like.

LATONA -- daughter of the Titans Coeus and Phoebe and mother by Zeus of Apollo and Artemis. She was abandoned by Zeus and wandered over the earth until she came to the island of Delos where Apollo was born and where, afterwards, his temple was located. (Crust).

LEAENA -- a courtesan of Athens. (Ann).

LEDA -- wife of Tyndareus, king of Sparta, and mother of Castor and Pollux, and of Clytemnestra and Helen of Troy. (Moll), *Ledidae* (Moll). Beauty.

LEMUR(ES) OR LARVAE -- spirits of the wicked dead as opposed to the Manes (q.v.) and greatly feared. Equivalent to the Greek *Lamia* above. Hence ghostlike, nocturnal. (Mam), *Lemuridae, Lemurinae, Lemuravus, Lemuravidae, Lemuroidea* (Mam), (Ins). *Lemuria* -- a hypothetical land bridge connecting Africa, Madagascar, and the East Indies. *Lemurphthinus* (Ins).

LERNA -- a marsh in Argolis where the Hydra (q.v.) dwelt. *Lernae, Lernaeascus, Lernaeidae, Lernaeodiscus, Lernaeophoda, Lernaeopidae, Lernanthropus, Lernentoma, Lerneocaera, Lerneomyzon* (Crust). Hydra-like.

LETHE -- river of Forgetfulness in the Underworld (Cf. Introduction). *Lethenteron* (Cyclost), *Lethocerus* (Ins), *Lethogrammus* (Pisc).

LETO -- same as *Latona*. (Ins).

LEUCIPPE -- daughter of Thestor. (Crust).

LEUCIPPUS -- father of Phoebe. (Av).

LEUCOTHOE -- daughter of Orchannus, king of Babylonia, changed by Apollo into a sweet-scented shrub. (Pl. sweet-scented), (Crust), *Leucothoella* (Crust).

LEUCOTHEA -- a sea nymph, identified with Ino (q.v.), mother of Palaemon. (Moll).

LIRIOPE -- mother of Narcissus. (Coel).

LODOICEA -- same as *Laodicea* (q.v.). (Pl). *Lodoicea maldivida* (Pl), double cocoanut supposed to have come from a tree at the bottom of the sea. Only the king was allowed to own up to 1759. As much as 400 L given for a specimen. (Thanks to Dr. Walter L. Buswell, University of Miami).

LUCIVER -- "light-bearer" -- the Day Star. (Crust). *Cocytius lucifer* (Ins).

LUCINA -- 1) same as Eileithyia, goddess of Childbirth; 2) epithets of both Juno and Diana. (Moll), *Lucinaea* (Pl. white, shining appearance, from Diana, the moon-goddess), *Lucinidae* and *Lucinacea* (Moll). *Lucinopsis* (Moll).

LYCAENA -- epithet of Venus. (Ins), *Lycaenidae* (Ins).

LYCORIS -- a Roman actress. (Ann), *Lycorea* (Ins), *Lycoridae* (Ann), *Lycorine* (alkaloid from *L. radiata*).

LYNCEUS -- 1) one of the Argonauts; 2) a cattle owner stabbed by Pollux; 3) husband of Hypermnestra, one of the Daniids (q.v.). (Mam), *Lynceidae* (Crust), *Lyncodaphniidae* (Crust).

M

MEANDER -- a winding river in Phrygia into which Hercules threw Lityerses. *Maeandrina* and *Maeandruseries* (Coel. "Brain Corals" from convolutions), *Maeandrusa* (Ins), *maeandrine*, *maeandriform*, *maeandrinoid* (winding, convoluted).

MAIA -- 1) a daughter of Atlas and mother of Hermes; 2) one of the Pleides; 3) wife of Vulcan, sometimes called Bona Dea and Fauna (q.v.) (Crust), *Maiidae* (Crust), *Maiopsis* (Crust).

MANIS -- singular of Manes, the Spirits of the Good in the Underworld, sometimes worshipped as gods. (Mam), *Manidae* and *Manitheria* (Mam). Habit of hiding in holes during day and feeding at night.

MARDONIUS -- a Persian general. (Myr).

MARCIA OR MARECA -- a nymph, mother of Latius. (Av. aquatic).

MEDUSA -- one of the Gorgons (q.v.) whom Perseus slew by cutting off her head which he gave to Athene who bore it upon the shield of Zeus. In biology: 1) the free-swimming, sexual generation of some Coelenterates, characterized by numerous tentacles; 2) a combining form used in names of animals having tentacles or snake-like appendages. *Medusaster* (Echin), *Medusoides* (Prot), *Hydromedusa* (Coel and Rept), *Leptomedusa* (Coel), *Limnomedusa* (Amph), *Pelomedusa* and *Pelomedusidae* (Rept), *Phyllomedusa* (Amph), *Caput medusae* (Pl. A mushroom and a Euphorbia with numerous drooping branches). *Medusa Bud* (structure on hydroid destined to become a medusa). *Medusiform* (having shape of medusa).

MELICERTES -- son of Athamas and Ino (q.v.). He was killed by his father. Ino took him into her arms and jumped into the sea. Both were turned into divinities. Also known as Palaemon. *Melicerta, Melicertidae, Melicertaceae* (Troch), *Melicertum* (Coel).

MEMNON -- 1) king of Ethiopia killed by Achilles in the battle of Troy and changed by his mother, Aurora, into a bird; 2) Greek name of Amenhotep III, king of Egypt. (Arach).

MENELAUS -- brother of Agamemnon, husband of Helen of Troy and king of Sparta. When he was courting Helen (daughter of Zeus and Leda and the world's most beautiful woman), who had many suitors, her reputed father, King Tyndareus, made them promie that they would come to the aid of whomever won her hand. Accordingly, when Paris (q.v.) stole her away from Menelaus, all the suitors rallied around him and leagued together to attack Troy. (Ins).

MERCURIUS -- Roman god identified with Hermes (q.v.). *Mercurialis* (Pl. from which a drug used as a diuretic is extracted), *Mercury* (chemical element which flows easily). Swiftness.

MERIONES -- a companion of Idomoneus (q.v.). (Mam. according to Jaeger, but possibly from "meria" -- thigh bone -- from peculiar formation of hind legs.

MEROPE -- 1) one of the Pleides; 2) wife of Cresphontes, king of Messenia and a son of Hercules. (Pl), (Moll).

MESSAPUS -- prince of Messapia. (Arach).

METON -- Athenian astronomer, discoverer of the Metonic Cycle, a period of nineteen years when the new moon returns on the same day of the year. It is the basis of the Greek calendar and of the Golden Numbers used in determining the date of Easter. *Meto* (Coel) and *Meta* (Arach which weaves an orb-shaped web, though the latter may be from METIS (Constructive thought), wife of Zeus before Hera. She told Zeus that the child she was carrying would be greater than he. He changed her into a fly and swallowed her but the child, Athene (q.v.), leaped forth from his head in a panoply of gold.

MEZENTIUS -- Etruscan king who was so cruel that he had been banished by his own people. He used to tie living persons to corpses for punishment. He joined the Latins against Aeneas, for which reason the Etruscans allied themselves with the latter. (Arach).

MIDAMUS -- one of the sons of Egypt. (Arach).

MIDAS -- king of Mygdonia who was given the power of turning anything he touched into gold. Later for having preferred the piping of Pan to the playing of Apollo, the latter gave him the ears of an ass as a sign of his stupidity. Also called Mydas (q.v.). (Mam has tufts on ears making them resemble those of an ass).

MIMMALONIDES -- one of the Bacchantes. (Ins).

MINERVA -- Roman goddess identified with Athene (q.v.). (Pl).

MOIRAE -- the three Fates: Clotho, Lachesis and Atropos. *Moira*. (Echin). *Moiraster* (Echin), *Miomoiera* (Ins), *Moeraphora* (Ins).

MOLOCH -- Phoenician god worshipped with human sacrifices. (Rept. from horrendous appearance).

MORPHO -- a name of Venus. (Ins), *Morphoides* (Ins). Beauty.

MUTINUS -- a name of Priapus (q.v.). (Pl. the "Dog-phallus Stinkhorn" fungus. (From shape).

MYDAS -- same as *MIDAS* (q.v.). (Rept. from yellow color), (Ins), *Mydaidae* (Ins).

MYRMIDON -- one of the followers of Achilles in the Trojan War. They received their name from a legend that when the population of the Island of Aegina (q.v.) was decimated by Hera out of jealousy of the girl after whom the island was named, King Aecus, her son by Zeus and the grandfather of Achilles, prayed to his father to change the ants (*myrmex*) into men to repeople the island. He did so and they were called *Myrmidons*. They were brave fighters. *Myrmedonia* (Ins. that fight ants).

MYRTAEA -- a name of Venus. (Moll), *Myrtale* (Arach). Beauty.

N

NAIAS -- one of the Naiads or Naids, water nymphs who dwelt in brooks, springs and fountains. (Pl), *Naiadaceae* (Pl), *Naiadae* (Moll), *Naiadales* (Pl), *Naiadina* and *Naiadites* (Moll), *Naiadochelys* (Rept). Aquatic habitat.

NAIS -- a fountain nymph; variation of *Naias*. (Ann), *Naidea, Naididae, Naidomorpha* (Ann). Same. *Naidium* (Ann).

NAPAEA -- a wood nymph. (Pl), *Napaeus* (Moll), *Napeozapus* (Mam), *Napochus* (Ins), *Napodonictis* (Mam), *Napomyia* (Ins), *Napophila* (Av). Forest habitat.

NARCISSUS -- 1) a handsome youth who scorned women until Nemesis made him fall in love with his own reflection in a pool. Since he could not satisfy his desire, he pined away. Where he died there sprang up a beautiful flower; 2) a purple and silver flower specially created by Zeus to enable his brother Hades (q.v.) to win Persephone (q.v.). One day when the latter was gathering flowers she spied this extraordinary blossom and, when she stooped to pick it, the earth opened and the god of the Underworld in a chariot drawn by black horses came forth and snatched her up and bore her away. (Pl). *Narcissism* (sexual perversion in which the object of love is oneself).

NAUSITHOE -- one of the Nereids (q.v.). (Coel).

NEAERA -- a girl mentioned by Horace. (Moll) and Nearomya (Moll). Beauty.

NECTAR -- "death-overcoming" drink of the gods. A sweet secretion of flowers from which bees make honey. *Nectar Gland* (Nectar-secreting), *Nectary* or *Nectarium* (part of flower containing Nectar Glands), *Nectandra* (Pl. having Nectar Glands), *Nectarinea* and *Nectarinidae* (Av. honey-eating), *Nectarine* (a kind of peach).

NEMERTES -- a Nereid (q.v.). (Platy) and combining form of genera, e.g., *Geonemertes* (Platy), -*nemertea* (combining form of old orders, e.g., *Paleonemertea*), *Nemertinea* (Platy), -*nemertini* (combining form of new orders, e.g., *Protonemertini*), *nemertean, nemertian* and *nemertoid* (relating to Nemertinea), *Nemertodrilus* and *Nemertoscolex* (Ann. similar to Nemertes).

NEMESIS -- Goddess of Retributive Justice and name of the snapdragon. *Nemesia* (Pl).

NEMESTRINUS -- god of groves. *Nemestrina* and *Nemestrinidae* (Ins). Habitat.

NEPENTHES -- a drug "removing all sorrow" given to Helen of Troy in Egypt. (Pl) and *Nepenthaceae* (Pl) from insect-killing digestive juices.

NEPHELE -- consort of Athamas and mother of Phrixus and Helle (Cf. Ino). *Nephila* and *Nephilinae* (Arach), *Nephelis* (Ann).

NEPHTHYS -- Egyptian goddess associated with ritual of the dead. (Ann), *Nephthydidae* (Ann), *Nephthya, Nephthyidae* and *Chironephthya* (Coel), *Nephthytis* (Pl).

NEPTUNUS -- Roman equivalent of Poseidon, god of the sea, Zeus' brother and husband of Amphitrite. He is represented as carrying a Trident. (Crust), *Neptunea* and *Neptunella* (Moll), *Poterion neptuni* (Por), *Thalassema neptuni* (Geph), *Neptunia* (Pl), *neptunism* (Werner's theory that all the rocks of the earth's crust were formed by the agency of water. Opposed to Plutonism (q.v.). Marine habitat.

NEREIS -- one of the Nereids, fifty sea nymphs, daughters of Nereus, the Old Man of the Sea, and Doris (q.v.), and attendants on Poseidon. The most famous were Amphitrite and Thetis, mother of Achilles. (Ann), *Heteronereis* and *Nereidae* (Ann), *Nereicalidae* (Crust. parasitic on Nereis), *Nereidaster* (Echin), *Nereidiformia* (Ann), *Nereilepas* (Ann), *nereite* (fossil worm track), *Nereites* (fossil Ann), *Nereocystis* (Pl), *Nereograptis* (Coel), *Nerine* (Pl and Moll), *Nerinea, Nerineidae* and *Nerita* (Moll), *neritic* (belt of shallow water adjoining coast; opposed to pelagic and oceanic), *Neritidae* (Moll), *Neritina* (Ann and Moll), *Neritoma, Neritopsis* (Moll). Marine habitat.

NESAEA -- a Nereid. (Pl). Marine habitat.

NESTOR -- king of Pylos and oldest of the Greek chieftains in the Trojan War. He was renowned for wisdom. (Av), *Nestoridae* and *Nestorinae* (Av), *Nestoritherium* (Mam). Age and wisdom.

NETHRUS -- goddess of Earth. (Pl).

NICOTHOE -- one of the Harpies (q.v.). (Crust). Eagle-like rostrum.

NIMROD -- a mighty hunter. *Nimravus* (Mam with huge teeth).

NINA -- a sea goddess. (Moll), *Ninella* (Moll). Marine habitat.

NIOBE -- daughter of Tantalus (q.v.) and wife of Amphion, who set herself above the gods for which cause her seven sons and seven daughters were killed. She was turned into stone and from her eyes tears constantly flowed. (Pl and Tril), *Niobella* (Tril). Stony.

NISUS -- king of Megara, changed into a sparrow hawk or sea eagle. (Av), *Nisaetus* (Av), *Nisuella* (Av). Hawks.

NYMPH OR NYMPHA -- "a bride" -- one of the inferior divinities, represented as beautiful maidens dwelling in meadows, forests and waters. *Nymph* (preadult stage of some insects), *nympha* (marginal process behind the beak of many bivalves), *nymphae* (labia minora of vulva), *Nymphaea* and *Nymphaeacea* (Pl), *Nymphaletes, Nymphalis, Nymphalidae, Nymphalides* and *Nymphalinae* (Ins), *Nymphaster* (Echin), *Nymphicus* (Av), *Nymphidina, Nymphipara* (obs. for Pupipara) (Ins), *Nymphoides* (Pl), *nymphomania* (excessive sexual desire), *Nymphophidium* (Rept), *Nymphopsis* and *Nymphopsinae* (Arthrop), *nymphosis* (change into a nymph), *Nymphostola* (Pl), *Nymphotrochtes* (Ins). Beauty or nymph formation.

Allied is Nymphon -- "bridechamber" -- (Arach. and in combining form, e.g., *Boreonymphon*), *Nymphonacea* and *Nymphonidae* Arach), *Nymphonella* (Ins).

NYX, NYCTOS -- Night, either uncreated and represented as a black-winged bird hovering over a vast darkness, or the offspring of Chaos. Cf. Introduction. It is used in many combinations signifying dark color or nocturnal habit. Must not be confused with onyx (claw) forming last part of many names, e.g., Clitonyx. *Nyctago* (Pl), *Nyctala* (Av), *Nyctalups* (Av), *Nyctalemon* (Ins), *Nyctanassa* (Av), *Nyctea* (Av), *Nyctemeridae* (Ins), *Nycteolinae* (Ins), *Nyctibatrachus*, *Nyctimantis* and *Nyctixalus* (Amph), *Nyctibiinae* and *Nyctibius* (Av), *Nyctiborides* (Ins), *Nycticebus* and *Nycticeius* or *Nycticejus* (Mam), *Nycticorax* and *Nyctidromus* (Av), *Nyctiellus*, *Nyctinomus*, *Nyctipithecus* (large eyes like lemur), *Nyctophilinae*, *Nyctophilus* (Mam), *Nyctornis* (Av), *Calonyction* (Pl). Allied are: 1) *Nycteris* -- "bat" -- (Mam); 2) *nycteros* -- "nocturnal" -- *Nycterbia*, *Nycteribia*, and *Nycteribiidae* (Ins), *Nycterobius* (Mam), *Balionycterus* (Mam); 3) *Nyctereutes* -- "one who hunts by night" -- (Mam); and 4) *nycterinos* -- "belonging to the night" *Nycterinea* (Pl).

O

OBERON -- king of the Fairies, husband of Titanis. *Oberonia* (Pl), *Oberonus* (Ins).

OCEAN OR OCEANUS -- a Titan (q.v.), lord of the river Ocean which encircled the earth. The Oceanids were his and Tethys' (q.v.) daughters and nymphs of the river. *Oceanapia* (Por), *Oceania* (Coel), *Oceanicus*, *Oceanites*, *Oceanitinae*, and *Oceanodroma* (Av). Habitat. *Ocean Bug* (*Halobates* -- found on surface of ocean far from land).

OEDIPUS -- son of Laius, king of Thebes, and Jocasta. Apollo foretold that he would kill his father and marry his mother. So Laius had him exposed, but he was brought up by strangers and later unknowingly committed the crimes prophesied of him, for which terrible punishments were visited upon Thebes until Oedipus put out his own eyes and resigned the throne. Sophocles has two tragedies on the subject: *Oedipus Tyrannus* and *Oedipus Colonus*. *Oedipus Complex* (sexual perversion in which a son has an unnatural love for his mother), *Oedipodium* (Pl), *Ooedipunidas*, *Oedipus* (Mam). *Edipism* (self-infliction of injury to the eyes).

OGYGES -- king of Athens in whose reign a great flood occurred. *Ogygopsis* (Arach).

OGYCIA -- island home of Calypso. (Tril).

OLENUS -- husband of Lethaea. Both of them were turned to stone. (Tril), *Olenus Zone* (Upper Cambrian characterized by trilobites of genus *Olenus*), (Tril), *Olenellus Zone* (horizon of early Cambrian characterized by *Olenellus*), *Olenelloides*, *Olenidae* (Tril). Fossils.

OLYMPUS -- home of the gods, first identified with a mountain of the same name in Thessaly, but later conceived as a region far above the earth. The entrance was guarded by the four Horae (q.v.) or Seasons. No wind blew, no rain or snow fell there, but the cloudless firmament stretched on all sides and the white glory of the sunshine diffused upon its walls. The same name has been given to a mountain and peninsula in the state of Washington (U.S.A.) and to a number of species inhabiting that region, e.g., *Marmota caligata olympus*, *Aplodontia rufa olympica*, *Spirogale phenax olympica*, *Glaucomys olympicus*, *Phenocomys olympicus* (Mam), and *Rycotriton olympicus* (Amph).

OMPHALOS -- "knob" or "boss" -- an altar of conical form at Delphi supposed to be the center of the earth. The *navel, omphalo* -- (relating to the navel).

OPHIUSA -- a name of Cynthus. (Ins).

OPIMIA -- a Vestal Virgin who was burned alive. (Crust).

ORCUS -- Roman god of Death (Thanatos). *Orca, Orcella, Pseudorca* (Mam). Killers.

OREAS -- one of the Oreads, nymphs of the mountain. (Pl and Mam == Taurotragus).

ORITHYIA -- sister of Procris carried away by Boreas (q.v.) (*Arthrop*).

ORONTES -- river in Syria famous in history. *Orontium* (Pl aquatic habitat).

OSIRIS -- Egyptian deity, husband of Isis (q.v.). (Ins).

OSMUNDER -- Saxon god. *Osmunda, Osmundaceae* (Pl. "Osmund Fern").

P

PAEON -- physician to the gods, attributed to both Apollo and Asclepios. *Paeonia* (Pl).

PALAEMON -- another name of Melicertes (q.v.). (Crust), *Palaemonetes* and *Palaemonidae* (Crust).

PALAMEDES -- hero of the Trojan War. *Palamedea, Palamedeae*, and *Palamedeidae* (Av).

PALINURUS -- pilot of Aeneas who fell asleep at the helm and went overboard. (Crust), *Palinuridae* (Crust), *Palinurichthys* (Pisc). Aquatic habitat.

PALLAS -- name of Athena (q.v.) *Micropallas* (Av. "Elf Owl").

PALLENE -- peninsula in Macedonia where the gods and giants battled. Probably named after Pallas. (Arthrop), *Pallenidae, Pallenopsis, Parapallene* (Arthrop).

PAN -- son of Hermes, part animal with goat horns and hoofs. God of shepherds and a musician ("Pipes of Pan"). (Mam. The Chimpanzee. Evolutionary significance).

PANACEA -- daughter of Aeculapius, goddess of healing. A cure-all.

PANDARUS -- son of Lycaon and hero of the Trojan War. (Ins).

PANDION -- king of Athens and father of Philomela and Procne (q.v.). (Av) and *Pandionidae* (Av. ospreys).

PANDORA -- "gift of all" -- the first woman created by Zeus. The gods gave her a box in which each placed some evil thing and warned her not to open it. But curiosity got the better of her and she lifted the lid and out flew numerous evils to plague mankind. (Moll) (Cten), *Pandorea* (Pl), *Pandoridae* (Moll), *Pandorina* (Pl and Prot). Box shape.

PANOPE -- a Nereid. (Moll), *Panopeus* (Crust), *Neopanope* (Arthrop).

PAPHIA -- name of Venus from Paphos, city of Cyprus sacred to her. (Moll and Ins), *Paphinia* (Pl). Beauty.

PAPHOS -- City of Cypru sacred to Venus. *Protoparce paphus* (Ins).

PARCAE -- three Roman birth goddesses corresponding to the three Moirae (q.v.) or Fates of the Greeks. *Protoparce* (Ins).

PARIS -- son of Priam, king of Troy. Eris, the goddess of Discord, threw a golden apple marked "for the Fairest" into the banquet hall at the wedding of King Peleus and Thetis. All of the goddesses wanted it, so Hera, Aphrodite and Pallas Athena called on Paris to judge which among them should have it, offering him various rewards, that of Aphrodite being the hand of the most beautiful woman in the world. Paris awarded it to Aphrodite ("The Judgment of Paris") and was given Helen of Troy, wife of Menelaus (q.v.). This was the supposed cause of the Trojan War. (Pl), *Parisis* (Coel).

PARNASSUS -- mountain in Greece sacred to Apollo and the Muses. During the great deluge only its top remained above the waters and there mankind was saved. At its foot lies Delphi. (Ins), *Parnassia* (Pl), and *Parnassinae* (Ins).

PARTHENOPE -- a Siren (q.v.) who threw herself into the sea because she could not win Odysseus with her songs. (Crust), *Parthenopa* (Mam), *Parthenopaea* and *Parthenopidae* (Crust). Aquatic habitat.

PARTHENOS -- "maiden" -- epithet of Athena, the "Virgin Goddess," whose temple in Athens was the "Parthenon." *Parthena* (Moll), *parthenogenesis* (development of the egg without fertilization).

PASIPHAE -- sister of Circe (q.v.), wife of Minos and mother of Ariadne and the Minotaur (Cf. Labyrinth). (Ins), *Pasiphaea* and *Pasiphaeidae* (Crust).

PEGASUS -- a winged horse said to have sprung from the Medusa's blood. Bellerophon (q.v.) bridled him with a golden bridle given him by Athena and rode him on many an adventure. But he was too ambitious and tried to ride him to the top of Olympus (q.v.), whereat Pegasus threw him off, but himself found shelter in the heavenly stalls and became the steed of the Muses. Hence the use of the term in connection with the writing of poetry. (Pisc), *Pegasidae*, *Parapegasus* (Pisc). Winged fins.

PELIAS -- son of Tyro who sent Jason in quest of the Golden Fleece, which came from the ram that saved Phrixus and Helle (Cf. Ino). He had usurped the throne of Jason's father (the uncle of Phrixus) and when Jason came to reclaim it Pelias thought to get rid of him by sending him on this quest. He was later killed by Jason's wife. (Rept. == Vipera). Bad repute.

PELOPS -- son of Tantalus (q.v.), boiled by his own father and served to the gods. He was restored to life and won Hippodamia (q.v.) for his wife by defeating her father, King Area, in a horse race. (Arach), *Pelopaeus* (Ins. "Hunting Wasp" which kills spiders), *Peleopsis* (Arach).

PENELOPE -- wife of Odysseus. During his absence many suitors sought her hand, but she put them off by saying that she would not marry anyone until she had finished weaving a shroud for Laertes, her father-in-law. But she never finished because at night she would unweave all that she had woven during the day. (Av), *Penelopides*, *Penelopina* and *Penelopinae* (Av). Weaving habit. *Eacles penelope* (Ins).

PENEUS -- river god, father of Daphne (q.v.) (Crust), *Penella*, *Peneidea*, *Peneidae*, and *Parapeneus* (Crust). Aquatic habitat.

PENTHEUS -- son of Cadmus and king of Thebes who imprisoned Dionysius (Bacchus) for introducing the "bacchanalia" into his kingdom and was torn to pieces by the latter's followers. (Crust).

PERSA -- daughter of Ocean. (Ann). Habitat..

PERSEPHONE (PROSPERINA) -- daughter of Zeus and Demeter, carried off by the lord of the Underworld (Cf. Narcissus). As a result Demeter withheld her gifts (Cf. Ceres) from the earth which was left desolate. Later Zeus ordered Persephone restored to Demeter except for four months each year when she must return to her husband in the Underworld. During this time Demeter punishes the earth with Winter. When Persephone returns to her it is Spring. *Persephona* (Crust).

PHAETON -- child of the Sun (Helios) and Clymene (q.v.). One day he climbed to the palace of the Sun and saw his father who asked him what gift he wanted. Phaëton asked to drive his father's chariot for a day. Helios tried in vain to dissuade the boy telling him of the difficulties of the task but he insisted and the father gave in. So he set out on the journey, but had not gone far when he lost control of the horses. They ran away and set the world on fire. Zeus struck Phaeton with a thunderbolt and he fell into the river Evidanus, along whose banks his sisters, the Heliades, turned into poplar trees, mourn him. (Ins. beauty), (Av), *Phaëthontidae*, *Phaëthornis*, *Phaëthura*, and *Phaëthurinae* (Av. tropical).

PHAON -- a youth of Lesbos beloved by Sappho (q.v.). (Ins) (Av. connection with Sappho).

PHARAO -- title of Egyptian kings. *Pharaonaster* (Echin), *Pharaonella* (Moll), *Pharaonis* (Moll). Probably Egyptian habitat.

PHARNACES -- king of Pontus. *Pharnaceum* (Pl).

PHEMENOE -- daughter of Apollo, first "Pythia" (q.v.), and inventor of hexameter verse. (Coel), (Av song), (Ins).

PHERECYDES OR PHERECIDES -- instructor of Pythagoras, a mathematical philosopher. (Arach. complicated web).

PHERUSA -- a Nereid. (Moll), *Pherusidae* (Moll). Marine habitat.

PHIALE -- companion of Diana. (Arach), *Phiala* (Ins).

PHIDIPPUS -- grandson of Hercules. (Arach), *Phidippia* (Arach).

PHILEMON a poor man who, with his wife, Baucis, unknowingly entertained Zeus and Hermes in their humble cottage, for which they were rewarded by being made priest and priestess of a temple and at death were turned into an oak and a linden, both of which grew from the same trunk. (Av).

PHILOMELA -- the sister of Cecrops and Procne (q.v.). The latter's husband, Tereus, seduced her and then cut her tongue out so that she could not tell Proche. But she got around the impediment by weaving the story on cloth and showing it to Procne. The latter revenged the two of them by killing her son, Itys, and serving his flesh to Tereus. When the latter learned of this crime, he pursued the sisters to Daulis (Cf. Daulias) to punish them but they were turned into birds. The original story was that the tongueless Philomela was changed into a swallow, which does not sing, and Procne into a nightingale. Later their roles were switched and now Philomela is the nightingale. (Av). Beautiful singer.

PHOENIX -- mythical bird which, when burned to death, would arise from its ashes. *Pseudophoenix* (Pl).

PHOLOE -- mountain in Thessaly where the Centaurs (q.v.) lived. (Ann).

PHORONIS -- another name of Io (q.v.). (Phor), *Phoronaria, Phoronidea, Phoroniella* (Phor), *phoronic acid* (derived from *Phoronidea*), *Phoroncidia* and *Phoroncidiinae* (Arach).

PHYLLODOCE -- a sea nymph. (Pl and Ann), *Phyllodoididae* (Ann), *Phyllodocites* (Ann). Marine habitat.

PICUMNUS -- god of fertility, associated with Pilumnus (q.v.). (Av), *Picumna* (Ins).

PIERIS -- one of the Pieridae or Muses, daughters of Zeus and Mnemosyne (Memory), born in Pieria in Thessaly. (Ins) (Pl), *Piercolias, Pierella, Pieridae, Pierinae* and *Calopieris* (Ins). Beauty.

PILUMNUS -- god of the pestle, associated with Picumnus (q.v.). (Crust), *Pilumnoplax* (Crust). Pestle shape.

PLUTO -- same as Hades, god of the Underworld and of wealth. (Mam. black), *Plutonaster* (Echin), *Plutonia* (Moll), *plutonism* (theory that rocks formed by igneous fusion; opposed to *neptunism* q.v.), *Plutonothrips* (Anthrop).

PODALEIRIOS -- son of Asclepios (q.v.). *Podalarias, Podalaridae* (Ins), *Podalyria* and *Podalyrieae* (Pl).

POLLUX -- the other of the Dioscuri (Cf. Castor). *Kosmoceras pollus* (Mam).

POLYDORUS -- 1) son of Cadmus;   2) son of Priam.   *Polydora* (Ann), *Polydoridae* (Ann).

POLYMNIA OR POLYHYMNIA -- the Muse of Music. (Pl and Ann). Beauty.

POLYNOE -- one of the Nereids. (Ann), *Polynoidae* and *Polynoina* (Ann), Marine habitat.

POLYPHEMUS -- of the Cyclopes (q.v.), son of Poseidon, who lived in a cave in Sicily and tended sheep. Odysseus and his men were trapped by him in the cave, but escaped by putting out his eye with a burning stake and riding out of the cave on the underside of the rams. Later Aeneas had a similar narrow escape. Another story makes him the lover of Galatea (q.v.).   (Ins. large "eye" on wing), (Crust) (Rept), *Polyphemidae* (Crust).

POMONA -- goddess of orchards. A treatise on fruit trees. *Salmonella pomona* (Pl). Parasite of fruits.

PORTUNUS -- god of the harbor. (Crust), *Portunicephon* (Crust), *Portunidae* (Crust), *Portunion* (Crust). Habitat.

POSEIDON -- same as Neptune (q.v.).   *Posidonia* (Moll), *Posidonomya* (Moll). Marine habitat.

PRIAPUS -- god of fertility, son of Dionysius (Bacchus) and Aphrodite. One of the Numina. Represented with a large phallus. (Geph), *priapism* (condition in which penis tends to stay erected), *Priapismus* (Ins), *Priapodes* (Ins), *Priapulidae, Priapuloidea* and *Priapulus* (Geph). Phallus shape. *Os priapi* (penis bone).

PROCNE OR PROGNE -- sister of Philomela (q.v.), first a nightingale and later a swallow or martin.   (Av), *Prognaster* (Echin), *Prochias* (Av. swallow-like bill), *Hydroprocne* and *Psalidoprocne* (Av), *Hybopsis Procne* (Pisc).

PROETUS -- king of Argos, whose wife Anteia fell in love with Bellerophon. (Tril) and *Proetidae* (Tril).

PROMENEA -- a prophetess (Pl).

PROMETHEUS -- "forethought" -- son of the Titan Iapetus and brother of Atlas (q.v.).   He and his brother Epimetheus ("afterthought") took sides with Zeus against the other Titans, for which Epimetheus was given the task of creating man. But, as his name signifies, he was a scatterbrain, and gave all the best gifts, such as swiftness, to the animals. So Prometheus took a stem of the Giant Fennel (narthex) up to heaven and placed in it some of the Sun's fire and brought it to earth and gave it to man, thus making him superior to the animals and like the gods. Some say that because of this he was bound by Zeus to a rock in the Caucasus and an eagle was sent to eat away his liver. There he was visited and consoled by Io (q.v.).

Another story attributes his punishment to a trick he played on Zeus. He cut up an ox and put the good meat in one pile which he covered with the entrails, and in another pile, the bones covered with fat, and gave zeus his choice. Zeus chose the fat and when he found that underneath it was only bones he was angry.

A third story is that Fate decreed that Zeus was to have a son who would dethrone him but did not disclose to him who the mother would be. Somehow Prometheus came to know the secret and Zeus found out that he knew it and tried to persuade him to divulge it. But he was adamant and hence Zeus tried to get it from him by torture.

There are two accounts of Prometheus' release: one, that Chiron (q.v.) offered himself to Zeus as a sacrifice to atone for Prometheus' fault; the other, that Hercules slew the eagle and released him. He is the subject of two plays by Aeschylus, *Prometheus Bound* and *Prometheus Unbound*. His name has become synonymous for independence and daring. (Ins), *Promethea* (Ins. cocoon suspended with a silken thread). *Promethium*, Element 61.

PRONUBA -- goddess of marriage; also epithet of Juno. (Ins. peculiar sex organ, *bursa copulatrix*).

PROSERPINA -- Latin name of Persephone (q.v.). (Moll), *Proserpinella* and *Proserpinidae* (Moll).

PROTEUS -- a sea god, son of Poseidon, who had the power to change his form at will. (Prot and Amph), *Protea* (Pl), *Proteidae* (Amph), *proteiform* (changeable shape), *Proteolepas* (Crust), *Proteosoma* or *Hemoproteus* (Prot). Ability to change shape.

PSYCHE -- a beautiful girl with whom Cupid fell in love much to the displeasure of his mother Venus who plagued Psyche in many ways. But Zeus changed her into a goddess and thus made her acceptable to Venus. Cupid and Psyche were then formally married, the union of "Love" and the "Soul." She is represented with the wings of a butterfly and the name signifies both "soul" and "butterfly." (Ins), *Psychidae*, *Psychina* (Ins), *Psychine* (Pl. has butterfly-like appendages on the pods), *Psychoda* and *Psychodidae* (Ins), *Psychonyidae* (Ins), *Psyichthys* (Pisc. butterfly-shaped fins), *Halopsyche* and *Halopsychidae* (Moll. butterfly-shaped fins), *Helicopsyche* (Ins). *Micrurus psyches* (Rept).

PYTERELAS -- one of the hounds of Actaeon (q.v.). (Crust).

PYLAEMENES -- king of Paphlagonians. (Ins).

PYRACMON -- servant of Vulcan (q.v.). (Ins).

PYTHIA -- a priestess of Apollo at Delphi, so called because of serpents associated with the worship. (Moll), *Pytheas* (Por), *Pythina* (Moll).

PYTHON -- a serpent of Delphi who destroyed men and cattle and was killed by Apollo who, for that reason, is called "Pythian." (Rept), *Pytho* and *Pythidae* (Ins), *Pythonaster* and *Pythonasteridae* (Echin) *Pythonichthys* (Pisc) *Pythonidae*, *Pythoninae*, *Pythoniscus* and *pythonomorpha* (Rept), *pythoniform* (serpent-shaped). Serpents or having serpent shape.

PUPA (a baby or doll) -- the name given to Poppaea, wife of Nero, when, after her execution, she was deified. The chrysalis of the lepidoptera. *Pupidae*, *Pupella*, *Pupoides*, *Pupopsis*, *Bothriopupa* (Moll), *Pupipara* (Ins).

R

RAMA -- one of the incarnations of the Hindu God, Vishnu. *Ramapithecus* (Mam). Indian habitat.

RHEA -- daughter of Uranus and Gaea, sister and queen of Cronus, and mother of Zeus and many other gods, hence called "Mother of the Gods." It had been foretold that one of Cronus' sons would dethrone him, so he used to swallow each one as he was born. But when Rhea gave birth to Zeus she hid him and gave Cronus instead a stone wrapped in swaddling clothes. (Av), *Rheae*, *Rheidae*, *Rheiformes*, *Rheoideae* and *Rheornithes* (Av). Large size.

RHESUS -- king of Thrace who fought in the Trojan War. (Mam. according to Audebert (1797) name has no significance).

RUNCINA -- a goddess presiding over weeding, possibly from a tool of the same name used for that purpose. (Moll), *Runcinella* and *Runcinidae* (Moll). Shape. *Runcinate* (with divisions pointing toward the base).

S

SALII -- "Leapers" -- Roman priests of Mars who guarded the shield that fell from heaven in the reign of Numa. The rites included dancing. *Saliococcus*, *Saliosthethus* and *Salius* (Ins). Leaping or dancing. *Saliidae* (Arach).

SALMACHS -- 1) fountain of Caria said to make effeminate anyone who drank of it;
2) nymph of the above fountain who was united with Hermaphroditus (q.v.). (Echin and Mam), *Salmacopsis* (Echin).

SANI -- Indian god. *Sanitherium* (Mam. Indian habitat).

SAPPHO -- poetess of Lesbos (c.600B.C.). (Av. singer), *sapphism* (homosexuality in women; Lesbianism).

SARPEDON -- 1) king of Lycia, son of Zeus and Europa;
2) grandson of above and one of the Trojan leaders killed in battle. Zeus sent Apollo to anoint his body with Sleep and Death. (Arach. poison).

SATANAS -- the devil. (Mam. black and bearded like representations of Satan), *Satanellus* (Mam same).

SATURNUS -- Roman equivalent of Cronus, the most important of the Titans or Elder Gods, and husband of Rhea (q.v.). He was dethroned by Zeus. The Romans held that when this occurred, Saturnus fled to Italy and brought in the "Golden Age." His rites were the "Saturnalia" celebrated in mid-winter, at which time no war could be declared, gifts were given and masters and slaves ate at the same table. *Saturnalia* (Prot), *Saturnia* and *Saturniidae* (Ins. large sized moths, e.g., *Atlas, Cecropia, Io, Polyphemus* q.v.), *Saturninus* and *Saturnulus* (Prot). *Saturn* (old name for lead), *Saturn's Tree* (same as *Arbor Dianae*, a tree-like formation resulting when lead is placed in a silver (Diana) nitrate solution), *saturnine colic* (lead poisoning), *s. palsy* (paralysis resulting from lead poisoning), *saturnize* (l. to combine with lead; 2. to castrate).

SATYR -- a Roman god of the woodland, represented with the horns and hoofs of a goat. (Ins), *Satyridae, Satyrides*, and *Satyrinae* (Ins), *Satyrus* (Mam. evolutionary significance), *Satyrium* (Pl. the "Satyr Orchid") *satyriasis* and *satyrism* (excessive sexual desire), *satyromaniac* (one who has), *satyrion* (an aphrodisiac).

SCYLLA -- a maiden changed by Circe (q.v.) into a monster from whose body grew snakes and dogs' heads. She inhabited a cave on the Sicilian side of the Straits of Messina, opposite the whirlpool Charybdis (q.v.), and was a peril to mariners, for instance, Odysseus, Jason and Aeneas. (Crust), *Scyllaea* and *Scyllaeidae* (Moll. from resemblance of gills to snakes), *Scyllarus* (Crust).

SELENE -- Moon Goddess, merged in Artemis and Hecate (q.v.). Reference to white, shining appearance. (Pisc), *Protoselene* (Mam), *selene unguium* (lunula of nail), *Selenaria* (Ann), *Selenchlamys* (Moll), *Selenia* (Pl), *Selenecereus* (Pl "Night-blooming Cereus"), *Selenichnus* (Amph), *Selenichthys* (Cyclost. == Lamprididae), *Selenidera* (Av), *Selenidium* (Prot), *selenin* (anti-serum prepared from cultures, of *Diplococcus semilunaris*) *Selenipedium* (Pl), *Selenis, Selenites* and *Selenitidae* (Moll), *Selenium* (white, shining metal), *selenodont* (having molar teeth with crescent-shaped ridges on crown), *Selenodonta* (Mam, having selenodont condition), *Selenops* and *Selenopsinae* (Arach), *Selenostomum* (Prot), *selenotropism* (turning towards the light). *Actias selene* (Ins).

SEMELE -- daughter of Cadmus and Hermione (q.v.) and mother of Dionysius (Bacchus) by Zeus. She was struck dead by seeing Zeus in all his splendor, but when Dionysius was grown up he descended to the Underworld and brought her to Olympus where she was accepted as a goddess. (Pl), *Semelartemis, Semelina* (Moll), *Semeloseris* (Coel).

SEMONIA -- Roman goddess of crops. (Platy).

SERAPIS -- Egyptian god with the form of an ox.   (Ins), *Serapias* (Pl), *Seraptista* (Ins).

SERGESTES -- companion of Aeneas.   (Crust), *Sergestidae* (Crust), *Sergestria* and *Sergestriinae* (Arach).

SIBYLLA -- an oracle or priestess, the most famous being the Sibyl of Cumae who guided Aeneas through the Underworld and sold the Sibylline Books to Tarquin the Proud.   (Ins), *Sibyllina* (Ins), *Sibyllonautilus* (Moll).

SIDA -- one of the Danaids. (Crust), *Sididae* (Crust).

SIGALION -- Egyptian goddess of silence. (Ann), *Sigalionina* (Ann).

SILENUS -- leader of the Satyrs (q.v.) and attendant of Bacchus, represented as baldheaded, flatnosed and drunken.   He was the occasion of Midas's unhappy wish. (Mam. satyr-like appearance), *Silene* (Pl), *Silenia* (Moll).

SIREN -- one of the mythical creatures, represented with the head of a woman and wings, who lived on an island and enchanted sailors with their singing, thus luring them to death.   Orpheus saved the Argonauts (q.v.) from them by playing louder than their singing.   Odysseus saved his men by filling their ears with wax and lashed himself to the mast so that he would not be lured away.   In medieval mythology, the siren was a serpent with a deadly bite.   In teratology the term is applied to a monster with its lower limbs fused. (Amph. lacks hindlegs and forelegs rudimentary), *Sirenia* (Mam. hind limbs rudimentary), *Sirenidae* (Amph), *Sirenoidea* and *Sireonidei* (Pisc), *Sirenopyga* (Ins), *Lepidosiren* (Pisc. formerly classed as Amph).

SIRIUS -- the Dog Star who follows Orion. *Siriella* (Crust).

SISYPHUS -- son of Aeolus (or Autolycus) and king of Corinth. He incurred the wrath of Zeus because he revealed to Asopus (q.v.) that Zeus had stolen his daughter Aegina (q.v.).   For this he was punished in the Underworld by having to roll a heavy stone uphill which constantly fell back down. Hence the idea of incessant labor. (Arach).

SITA -- wife of Rama. *Sitana* (Rept. Indian habitat.)

SIVA -- Hindu god of destruction, represented with four arms. *Sivameles*, *Sivameryx*, *Sivapithecus*, *Sivatheriidae*, *Sivatherinae* and *Sivatherium* (Mam. last has two pairs of horns resembling God. But Ziegler and Bresslau derive from Siwalik stratum in which found.)

SMINTHUS -- "mouse" -- a name of Apollo, but not known whether because he protected them or destroyed them. (Mam. mouse-like).

SPHINX (SPHINGOS) -- a monster with the head and bust of a woman, the body of a lion and wings. The most famous was the one near Thebes who used to propose riddles to passersby and if they could not solve them, she would devour the unfortunates. Oedipus (q.v.) solved the riddle she gave him, namely, "What creature goes on four feet in the morning, on two at noonday, on three in the evening?," by answering "Man; for in childhood, he creeps on hands and feet; in manhood, he walks erect; in old age he helps himself with a staff." As a result, she killed herself and the Thebans were saved. There are many representations of the Sphinx, the most noted being that in Egypt. (Ins), *Sphingidae* and *Sphinginea* (Ins. "Hawk Moth" larva assumes position resembling Sphinx), *Sphingiurus* (Mam), *Papio sphinx* (Mam). *Pseudosphinx, Syssphinx* (Ins).

SPIO -- a Nereid. (Ann), *Spiochaetopterus* (Ann), *Spionidae* (Ann), *Spiosphagnes* (Ann). Marine habitat.

STENTOR -- a Grecian herald with a loud voice. (Prot. trumpet-shaped), (Mam. "Howling Monkey," sound due to saccular diverticula of the larynx).

STYX (STYGOS)-- river "of the unbreakable oath" in the Underworld across which the dead were ferried by Charon (Cf. Introduction). (Ins), *Stygia* and *Stygides* (Ins), *Styganodon* (Moll), *Stygicola* (Pisc. cave dwelling), *Stygina* (Tril), *Stygiochelifer* (Arach), *Stygogenes* (Pisc. formerly falsely believed to inhabit the subterranean waters of active volcanoes), *Stygnicranus* (Arach), *Stygnohydrus* (Ins), *Stygnus* (Arach). Subterranean habitat.

SYLLIS -- a nymph. *Sylla* and *Syllidae* (Ann).

SYLVANUS -- one of the Numina, the helper of plowmen and woodcutters. (Mam), *Sylvania* (Av), *Sylvanocochlis* (Moll). Forest habitat.

SYPHILUS -- Shepherd in poem of Fracastorius (1530), "Syphilis sive Murbus Gallicus," who bathed in a river of mercury. *Syphilis* -- a venereal disease caused by *T. pallidum*.

SYRINX (SYRINGOS) -- *"reed"* -- a nymph beloved by Pan and turned into a reed from which he fashioned his pipes. Applied to many pipe-shaped organisms and structures. (Geph. obs. for *Sipunculus*), *Syringa* (Pl), *Syringodea* (Pl), *Syringopora* (Coel), *Syringophilus* (Arach), *Syringothyris* (Moll), *Cymatosyrinx* (Moll).

T

TAGES -- Etrurian god who sprang from the earth and taught man the art of plowing. *Tagetes* (Pl may be misreading for *Traganthes*), *tagetol* and *tagetone* (chemicals from *Tagetes*).

TANTALUS -- son of Zeus and father of Pelops and Niobe (q.v.). He killed Pelops and served him to the gods. For this he was punished with hunger and thirst in the Underworld by being placed in a pool of water which would recede from him when he stooped over to drink. Over his head was a tree laden with fruit, but when he reached for it, it moved away. Hence "tantalize." (Av) and *Tantalops* (Av. possibly from difficulty in observing), *tantalite* ore from which is extracted *tantalum* (a metal "tantalizingly" difficult to extract).

TARQUINIUS -- name of two kings of Rome. *Dirphia tarquinia* (Ins).

TARTARUS -- the deeper of the two parts of the Underworld (Cf. Introduction). *Tartarothyas* (Arach).

TELEPHOS -- a Greek warrior who had a wound that would not heal. *Telephum* -- an ulcer that will not yield to treatment.

TETHYS -- wife of Ocean (q.v.) and ancient name of many sea animals. (Rept and Moll), *Tethys Sea* (hypothetical pre-Cambrian sea between North America and Gondwanaland), *Tethya* (Por), *Tethyidae* (Moll), *Tethymelibidae* (Moll), *Tethyodea* and *Tethyum* (Tun). Marine habitat.

TEUCER -- first king of Troy, whence Trojans called "Teucri." *Teucrium* (Pl), *teucrifolium* (Pl).

THAIS -- name of several courtesans, the most notable being the mistress of Alexander the Great and afterwards wife of Ptolemy Lagos. (Ins) (Moll. possibly because related to *Murex* from which royal purple was obtained.

THALES -- Greek philosopher. *Thalesia* (Pl).

THALIA -- 1) one of the three Graces; 2) the Muse of Comedy; 3) a Nereid. (Pl, Ins, Tun), *Thaliacea* and *Thalida* (Tun). Graceful beauty.

THAMYRIS -- a bard who challenged the Muses and was struck blind. (Crust).

THELPHUSA -- a nymph. (Crust), *Thelphusidae* and *Geothelphusa* (Crust).

THETIS -- one of the Nereids, wife of Peleus (Cf. Paris) and mother of Achilles. (Moll), *Thetisella* (Ann), *Thetopsis* (Moll). Marine habitat.

THYENE -- nurse of Zeus and Dionysius. (Arach), *Thyenillus* (Arach), *Thyenula* (Arach).

THYESTES -- son of Pelops who stole his brother Atreus' wife. For this Atreus killed Thyestes' children and served them to him. (Pisc).

THYONE -- mother of the fifth Bacchus. (Moll and Crust), *Thyanella* and *Thyonidium* (Echin).

TISIPHONE -- one of the Erinyes or Furies (q.v.), avenger of murder. (Rept), *Tisiphonia* (Coel).

TITANUS -- one of the Titans or Elder Gods who ruled the earth before Zeus and the Olympians. The most important was Cronus. They were overthrown by Zeus with the help of Prometheus (q.v.) and condemned to Tartarus, except Atlas (q.v.). Large size. (Mam), *Titanichthys* and *Titanichthyidae* (Pisc), *Titanideum* (Coel), *titanium* (chemical element with a high molecular weight), *Titanodamon* (Arach), *Titanomys* (Mam), *Titanops* (Av), *Titanophasma* (Ins),

Titanornis (Av), *Titanosaurus* (Rept), *Titanothere* or *Titanotherium* and *Titanotheridae* (Mam). *Amorphophallus titanum*, (Pl) -- great size.

TITHONUS -- husband of Aurora (Dawn) and father of Memnon (q.v.). Aurora asked Zeus to make him immortal, but forgot to ask also that he might remain young. So the older he grew the more he shrank in size until, at last, in pity, she changed him into a grasshopper (Ins), *Tithonia* (Pl), *tithonic* (actinic rays of sun).

TITYUS -- a giant, son of either Gaea or Zeus, slain by Apollo. In Hades two vultures eat his liver. (Arach), *Tityobuthus* (Arach), *Tityolepreus* (Arach).

TMOLUS -- a mountain and a god of Lydia who was chosen umpire in the contest between Apollo and Pan (Cf. Midas). (Ins).

TRITON -- son of Poseidon and Amphitrite and trumpeter of the sea. His trumpet was a conch shell, hence conch-like shape or trumpeting. (Amph. and combining form, e.g., Geotriton), *Tritonaster* (Echin), *Tritonia*, *Tritonidae*, *Tritonidea*, *Tritonidoxa*, *Tritonium* and *Tritonoharpa* (Moll), *Triturus* (Amph).

TRIVIA -- "three roads" -- name of Hecate (q.v.) as goddess of the Crossroads, represented with three heads and six arms. (Moll. shape).

TROILUS -- son of Priam, killed by Achilles. He seduced Cressida and she deserted him for Diomedes (q.v.). Cf. Shakespeare, *Troilus* and *Cressida*. (Ins).

TYCHE -- goddess of Luck (Fortuna). *Tychaeus* (Ins), *Tychlepsephemus* (Ins), *Tycherus* (Ins), *Tychestylous* (Mam), *Tychus* (Ins), *tychism* (theory of evolution according to which variations are purely fortuitous).

TYDAEUS -- father of Diomedes, hence called "Tydides," and one of the "Seven Against Thebes." These were seven chieftains led by Poly-neices, son of Oedipus, in an attack on Thebes to recover the throne from his younger brother, Eteocles. Only one, Adrastus, returned alive. (Arach). Fighter.

TYNDAREUS -- husband of Leda (q.v.). *Xylophanes tyndarus* (Ins).

TYPHOEUS -- a hundred-headed monster with fearful eyes who opposed Zeus and was struck with a thunderbolt and buried under Mount Aetna in Sicily. The eruptions of this volcano were said to be signs of his anger boiling up. According to some he was the same as Typhon; but according to others he was the father of Typhon, who begot Cerberus, the Chimaera, the Sphinx and other monsters of Echidna (q.v.), (Ins) and possibly *Typhaeus* (Ann).

TYRO -- daughter of Salmoneus. She bore twin sons, Pelias (q.v.) and Neleus, to Poseidon. When her husband Cretheus found out about this he divorced her and married Sidaro, her maid. The latter treated her cruelly and Pelias killed Sidaro. Tyro's son by Cretheus was the father of Jason (Cf. Argonaut). (Crust), *Tyroglyphus*, *Tyroglyphidae* and *Tyroglyphinate* (Arach).

U

UNICORN -- fabulous horse-like animal with one horn, first mentioned by Cresias (398 B.C.), physician to Artaxerxes II, after his return from Persia. Called "Monokeros" in Greek. Obsolete name of *Rhinocerus* and common name of many plants and animals with a single horn-like structure, e.g., *Unicorn Antelope*, *Beetle*, *Bird* (Horned Screamer), *Fish* (Narwhal and Filefish), *Moth* (*Schizura unicornis* -- larva has a horn), *Plant* (*Martynia louisiana* -- capsule has a beak), *Ram* or *Sheep* (has horns closely pressed together as a result of searing when young), *Root* (either *Chamelirum luteum* or *Helonias bullata*), *Shell* (Moll. *Monoceros* and *lativus*). During the Middle Ages "Unicorn Horn" was much used as an antidote against poisons. Two kinds were on the market, *Unicornum Verum* (Alicorn), thought to be Mammoth tusks, and *Unicornum Falsum*, Narwhal tusks. Even drinking from a cup made from a unicorn's horn was supposed to preserve from death by poison. (Cf. Ley, *The Lungfish and the Unicorn*).

URANIA -- 1) epithet of Aphrodite; 2) Muse of Astronomy. (Ins), Uraniidae (Ins). Bright colors.

URANUS or OURANOS -- "the sky" -- Father Heaven who begot of Mother Earth (Gaea) the first creatures, Titans, Cyclopes, etc. He was wounded by his son Cronus and from his blood sprang the Giants. *Uranichthys* (Pisc), *Uranium* (element), *Uranornis* (Av. "Bird of Paradise"), *Uranodon* (Mam), *Uranoscopus* and *Uranoscopidae* (Pisc. the "Star-gazers" -- eyes turned dorsally), *Ouranion* (Ins), *Ouranokyrtus* (Mam). *Uranism* (homosexuality among men), *urani-* and *urano-* (relating to the roof of the mouth -- *uraniscus*). *Uranops* (Pisc), *Uranotaenia* and *Uranotes*. (Ins).

V

VAMPYRUS -- a bloodsucking ghost. (Mam. blood sucking), *Vampyrella* and *Vampyrellidae* (Prot. ectoparasite).

VEJOVIS -- Etruscan god of the Underworld. (Arach) and *Vejovidae* (Arach).

VELEDA -- old German goddess. (Moll), *Veledella* (Ins), *Velleda* (Ins).

VENILLA -- 1) mother of Turnus; 2) wife of Jason. (Ins).

VENUS -- Roman goddess of Love and Beauty, equivalent of Aphrodite. (Pl. and Moll), *Veneracea* (Moll), *venereal* (relating to sex), *venereology* (branch of medicine treating of venereal diseases), *Venericardia* and *Veneridae* (Moll. beauty of shell), *veneriform* (having form of *Veneridae*), *Venerupis*,

Veniella, Venillicardia (Moll), *Capillus veneris* (Pl) *Cestus veneris* (Cten. shaped like a belt "cestus"), *Speculum veneris* (Pl).

VERTUMNUS -- "God of the Changing Year" -- lover of Pomona (q.v.) and joined with her in protecting gardens. (Crust).

VESPER -- same as Hesper (q.v.), the Evening Star. *Vesper Mouse* (Peromyscus), *Vespertillio, Vespertillionidae* and *Vespertillioninae* (Mam).   Nocturnal animals.

VISHNU -- Hindu God. *Vishnutherium* (Mam). Indian habitat.

VULCAN -- Roman equivalent of Hephaestus, god of Fire, son of Zeus and Hera. He was first thrown out of heaven because of his ugliness but later was made armorer (Mulciber) of the gods. He was the patron of blacksmiths. *Vulcanella* (Por), *Vulcanomyia* (Moll).

X

XOLOTL ("corn plant with two stalks") -- an Aztec god, twin of Quezacoatl, the patron of twins and monsters. He had protean ability which he used to escape from enemies, changing successively into *mexolotl* ("maguey with two bodies"), *texolotl* (stone pestle, considered the twin of the mortar), and *nexolotl* (turkey, considered a monster perhaps because of its crest). However, on the last occasion he jumped into the water and turned into the *axolotl* (considered a monster because of its neotonic nature) but was caught and killed. *Axolotl* (Amph). (From Martin del Campo, Rafael. 1946. *Xolotl y los Gemelos y Monstruos.* Ann. Inst. Biol. Mex., XVII (1-2):343).

Z

ZEPHYRUS -- the West Wind (L. Favonius). He it was who rescued Psyche (q.v.) from the winged serpent and bore her to Cupid.   (Ins), *Zephyranthes* (Pl).

ZETHUS -- son of Zeus and Antiop (q.v.) and brother of Amphion.   (Ins), *Zethoides, Zethusculus* (Ins).

ZEUS (Dios) -- chief of the twelve Olympians who overthrew Cronus, the Titan, and became lord of the universe and "Father of Gods and Men," the equivalent of the Roman Jupiter or Jove. Hera (Juno) was his sister and queen, but he had children by many mortal women. The eagle was his bird, the oak (*Aegilops* q.v.) was his tree, and Dodona "in the land of the oak trees," was his oracle, his will being manifested by the rustling of the oak leaves. His favorite child, Athena (q.v.), carried his shield, the Aegis, upon which was borne the Medusa's head given her by Perseus. A poetic form of his name is "Zen" and the diminutive "Zenion." (Pisc), *Zeidae, Zenion* and *Zenopsis* (Pisc).

ZOROASTER -- Persian prophet and founder of Zoroastrianism, a religion of dualism between Ormurazd, god of light and goodness, and Arihman, lord of darkness. (Echin), *Zoroasteridae* (Echin).